CW00815798

Cider Apple

Growers Guide

2nd Edition

Guidelines for integrated crop management of cider apples

Published by Liz Copas for the National Association of Cider Makers in association with ADAS, East Malling Research [EMR] and the Farming and Wildlife Advisory Group [FWAG]

Written and edited by
Liz Copas, NACM
Roger Umpelby, Fruit Entomologist
Angela Berrie, East Malling Research
With support from other members of the NACM Pomology Committee

© National Association of Cider Makers
First published April 2002
2nd Revised edition 2011

ISBN 978-0-9568994-0-8

CONTENTS

Disclaimer

The content of this booklet is published in good faith but neither the NACM nor the authors can accept any liability for loss or damage resulting from the application of any concept or procedure discussed in or derived from it.

Preface

The NACM Cider Apple Growers Guide is designed to present growers with a useful reference point for information on all aspects of modern cider apple growing. It is not intended as an instruction manual, but aims to encourage good agricultural practice.

By offering guidelines for integrated crop management of cider apple orchards, this booklet illustrates ways of rationalising and minimising pesticide use through increased awareness of the importance of cultural control methods, monitoring, prediction and assessment of potential problems.

Working to the best practices described will provide the reassurance that our orchards are managed to the highest standards to produce quality fruit for the cider industry, whilst giving full consideration to the environment, the customers and the growers themselves.

This second edition of the Guide, edited by Liz Copas for the NACM, has been compiled and updated by Roger Umpelby, ADAS, and Angela Berrie, EMR, with assistance from Chris Fairs, Bob Chaplin and John Worle. It incorporates current information from NACM and EMR research and development work.

It is intended that where required users should seek additional information for details of some subjects such as pests, diseases and current commercial products. An extensive list of other useful and informative sources is given.

The Guide has intentionally excluded any information that might go out of date, however where legislation may change, or other unforeseen subjects arise, any revisions and further information will be published in the Grower's Update.

National Association of Cider Makers
2011

CHAPTER 1

General introduction

In common with most other crops, cider apple production has changed considerably in recent years. Many of the changes have been a result of advances in technology and growing techniques, but changes in legislation, in customer requirements and in public expectation have all had a major impact. Additionally the economics of growing the crop have changed, particularly profit margins being squeezed, partly due to increased mechanisation costs and to labour being increasingly expensive. This means that, to be successful, growers need to produce regular and heavy crops using a system which minimises environmental risks, addresses all food safety issues, conforms to all current legislation, minimises hazards to workers and third parties but still provides the customer with the product they require.

This Guide is designed to provide growers with the outline of the areas and points that they need to consider in the whole process of planning, planting and particularly growing cider apples. It is designed only to give background information and is not intended to be a 'manual' of cider apple growing. For detailed advice on day-to-day growing there is a wealth of expertise available from independent consultancy organisations, individual consultants, cider makers and the whole range of associated supply industries. When seeking advice, be sure that those 'offering' it are suitably qualified and competent, there is no substitute for a personal recommendation!

Following the information within this Guide, growers will be addressing all of the current parameters which embrace some of the extensively used, but often misunderstood, terms such as Integrated Crop Management (ICM) and Integrated Pest Management (IPM). More importantly they will be undertaking Good Agricultural Practice, for which there are published Codes of Good Agricultural Practice covering air, water and soil (1988, MAFF).

CHAPTER 2

Planning and recording

For any business venture to have any chance of success thorough planning is essential, and planting of cider apple orchards is no exception. Once planted, recording of activities and associated operations not only makes sound business sense for planning the future and for your customer but, in many cases, keeping records is a legal requirement.

- Before finalising plans to plant a new cider apple orchard it is advisable to secure a market for the end-product

- There are a limited number of outlets for cider apples. Before planting, if possible secure a long-term contract with a cider maker for supply from the planned orchard

- In the absence of such a contract you will need to be convinced that there is likely to be sufficient demand for the fruit you are hoping to produce throughout the prospective life of the orchard

- Another fundamental requirement is that there is the capability, either on the farm or locally, to undertake all the necessary work in managing, growing, maintaining and harvesting the crop, including labour and equipment

- Cider apple orchards should only be planted on suitable sites (see Chapter 3) or the venture is likely to be uneconomic

- Having decided on a site the appropriate trees (cultivar and rootstock combination) should be ordered well in advance (ideally at least 2 years) from a professional nursery (see Chapter 4)

- Before ordering trees check that you have made adequate provision for pollinator cultivars

- Prepare a planting plan well in advance and include other factors such as drainage, windbreak and fencing at the earliest stage (see Chapter 5)

- Ensure that the proposed orchard is included in the long-term whole-farm conservation plan (see Chapter 12)

- All aspects of the planning process should be recorded for future reference. Drainage and other agronomic aspects are particularly important and should be retained indefinitely

- Once planting starts ensure that all significant operations are recorded and kept in an accessible format

- Annual records should be kept of all major orchard operations, and for certain activities, such as pesticide applications, these must be kept according to the current legislation

- Ensure that all other legally required records relating to the farm and its facilities, the staff and cropping operations (e.g. H&S facilities and training) are kept up-to-date
- Ensure that all customer requirements are met and appropriately recorded
- Thorough records will not only cover legal and customer needs, but will provide very valuable information for future management decisions

CHAPTER 3

Site selection

The major consideration for site selection will be the overall suitability for growing apples, but the location of the customer, the cider producer, will also have a significant bearing on the choice. Transport costs can form a major part of production costs and must be considered in the site selection decision-making process. Because the economics of cider apple production have changed considerably, the existence of established orchards is not necessarily a good indicator of the suitability of a locality for planting new orchards.

- Apples are tolerant of many different soil types, but require a good depth of soil to provide adequate anchorage, particularly when bearing a heavy crop

- As a general rule, sites with less than 0.5m (18")of good topsoil will be unsuitable for cider apple orchards

- Shallow soils may also restrict the depth to which stakes can be driven. Good stake anchorage is vital in the early years of an orchard

- Sites are normally recommended to be below a height of 120m (400 feet), but if other characteristics are very favourable, plantings can be considered at slightly higher altitudes

- If possible choose regular shaped fields to avoid having short tree rows which are difficult to manage

- Re-planting on old orchard sites can result in very poor and/or slow establishment due to a soil condition known as 'apple replant disorder', or ARD

- Planting between previous tree positions and rows may overcome the replanting problem, but the other effective options, such as soil sterilisation or replacing soil in the planting holes, are uneconomic

- Using sites which were previously woodland may result in substantial tree losses due to polyphagous and relatively persistent diseases such as *Armillaria,* and should be avoided

- It is unlikely that any site will be perfect for cider apple production, so some adverse characteristics do not necessarily rule the site out for planting and for establishment of a successful cider apple orchard

- Seek help from a well qualified professional consultant, either independent or your proposed customer, before making a final decision on planting

- Ideally a north-south row orientation should be used

- Avoid planting rows across steep slopes.

3.1 Soil type

- Apples will grow successfully on a relatively wide range of soil types
- Good intrinsic fertility retention is an advantage as it reduces the need for heavy annual applications of fertiliser. Soils with a low silt or clay content tend to be less retentive of nutrients
- Good anchorage is essential to prevent lodging and wind-rock (which causes root damage)
- The root damage caused by wind-rock allows easy access to soil-borne diseases such as *Phytophthora*, and may result in tree death
- Avoid heavy clay soil as establishment will be slow, drainage is inherently poor and root disease problems are more likely
- Soils with a high clay content are prone to compaction in the alleyways due to passage of heavy machinery and should be avoided
- Avoid very light sandy soils as anchorage in the early years may be poor and in dry years water stress may be a problem. Irrigation is possible but may be uneconomic on cider apples
- Light soils on steep slopes are very prone to surface erosion
- Very light soils are more prone to fertiliser leaching.

3.2 Drainage

- Drainage problems are extremely difficult to correct once an orchard is established
- Because apples are perennial and deep-rooted they will be more susceptible to poor drainage than most annual crops or pasture
- Where drainage is a possible problem ensure that this can be corrected before considering planting. Use a stone back-fill, ideally to the soil surface, but at least within 30cm of it.
- Sites with inherently poor drainage must be avoided.

3.3 Aspect

- The aspect of a site is not particularly important for cider apple production, but sites with variable aspects have certain disadvantages
- Sites facing north or east, generally take longer to dry out after rain etc. and are likely to be more prone to diseases such as scab or canker
- Exposed south west and west-facing sites are more likely to be affected by tree lodging and wind-rocking and the associated disease problems

- Very undulating sites where significant parts slope in different directions will cause problems with extended flowering periods restricting the application of pest and disease control sprays
- Very undulating sites may result in harvest scheduling problems due to different ripening rates and fruit maturity.

3.4 Topography

- Most cider apples flower considerably later than dessert or culinary apples and are much less prone to frost damage, but early-flowering cultivars will still be at risk
- Known frost pockets should be avoided
- Slopes tend to give natural assistance to air and water drainage problems
- Most of the operations in a cider apple orchard involve the use of tractor-powered machinery. When planting on steep slopes consideration must be given to the use of machines, particularly the safety aspects.

3.5 Climate

- The climate in the southern half of England and Wales will normally provide good conditions for the growth and ripening of cider apples
- In Devon and Cornwall where high humidity and milder winters encourage vegetative growth at the expense of cropping, careful management is needed to overcome this
- Ideally summer rainfall (April – September) should not exceed 400mm
- In high summer rainfall areas scab and canker are likely to be a problem (see Chapter 7)
- Exposure to wind can restrict growth and, due to abrasion and wind-rocking, increase occurrence of wood and root diseases.

CHAPTER 4

Tree selection

4.1 Cultivar (variety)

A cider cultivar is a distinct variety of apple, selected and cultivated primarily for cider making use. The apples may have a chewy flesh to facilitate juice extraction, a relatively high sugar content for alcohol production, tannin to provide a bitter or astringent taste, and a pleasing apple taste and aroma. Cider cultivars will fall into one of four broad taste classes with a distinct character according to the acid and tannin content of the juice. Sharp and bittersharp cultivars have juice with acidity greater than 0.45%. Sweet and bittersweet cultivars are normally well below this. Juices of bittersweets and bittersharps have tannin levels in excess of 0.18%, but sweet, sharp and juice apples contain relatively little tannin.

The pre-requisites of a good cider orchard tree are; precocious cropping to recoup capital outlay as quickly as possible; to produce regular and good crops with little biennial tendency; to be relatively pest and disease free to minimise spray inputs; and to have a good growth habit with a natural centre leader that requires minimal initial tree training.

Choice of cultivar depends on the cider maker's and the grower's requirements

- Cider maker's choice depends on: when the factory wants fruit and of which type; early or mid season; bittersweet / sharps / juicing cultivars
- Grower's choice depends on how he wants to spread the harvesting load, the cultivars best suited to his area and which cultivars might attract a premium price.
- Many cider makers no longer accept new plantings of the cultivar Michelin because of its poor juice quality and character in the mill. Contact your cider maker to make sure.

Performance of cultivars is influenced by conditions of site;

- Avoid very vigorous cultivars on strong soils (e.g. Major); avoid weak cultivars on heavier ground or shallow soils with restricted root run (e.g.Dabinett and Ashton Bitter)
- Avoid scab prone cultivars in wetter areas where the orchard microclimate is likely to be humid during the growing season (e.g. Michelin, Chisel Jersey, Stembridge Jersey, Coat Jersey)
- On cool, wet sites with heavy soil, avoid canker prone cultivars (e.g. Michelin and Browns Apple)

- Expect that more fungicide will be required to control mildew on susceptible cultivars (e.g. Michelin, Somerset Redstreak) in drier, inland areas of the West Midlands,
- Avoid planting large blocks of single cultivars unless their self-fertility is assured, and avoid large blocks of any single cultivar on windy or exposed sites where pollination conditions are likely to be sub-optimal
- Plant cultivars with a weak tree habit on more sheltered sites to avoid losing the centre leader through it blowing over in the prevailing wind (e.g. Ashton Bitter, Dabinett)
- Most cider apples flower later than the severest frosts and damage to the blossom of any suggested cultivars is unlikely in recommended locations.

Varietal differences

- For regular crops choose cider cultivars with a reliable annual cropping tendency (e.g. Dabinett, Michelin, Harry Masters Jersey, Yarlington Mill, Ellis Bitter etc.) A biennial cropping pattern may still build up as the orchard ages, but should be easier to control. Some useful, heavy cropping cultivars are inherently biennial and have to be accepted as such in return for potentially exceptional crops in alternate years (e.g. Browns Apple, Somerset Redstreak)
- For minimal tree training inputs, choose cultivars with a strong natural centre leader habit and lightweight primary lateral branches. Strong growing cultivars which produce much vigorous vegetative growth, will need greater inputs to encourage early and regular cropping
- For ease of management, do not mix cultivars together in single rows. Under most circumstances, 5 row blocks of each cultivar create more than adequate pollination conditions. This can usually be extended to larger blocks if the cultivar is reliably self-fertile
- For planting in adjacent blocks, choose cultivars with similar pest and disease spray requirements, and flowering and fruit harvesting season.

Season of fruit maturity

Early (end September - October)	Mid season (October)	Late (late October – November)
Ashton Bitter*	Browns Apple*	Dabinett
Browns Apple*	Harry Masters Jersey	Chisel Jersey
Ellis Bitter	Kingston Black	Yarlington Mill
Major	Michelin	
Somerset Redstreak*		
White Jersey	* cultivars with a marked biennial cropping tendency	

Varietal characteristics

Cultivar	Scab susceptibility	Mildew susceptibility	Self fertility
Ashton Bitter	Resistant	Susceptible	Poor
Browns Apple	Resistant	Susceptible	Good
Chisel Jersey	Susceptible	Susceptible	Poor
Dabinett	Susceptible	Susceptible	Good
Ellis Bitter	Slightly susceptible	Slightly susceptible	Fair
Harry Masters Jersey	Slightly susceptible	Slightly susceptible	Good
Kingston Black	Susceptible	Slightly susceptible	Poor
Major	Slightly susceptible	Resistant	Variable
Michelin	Susceptible	Susceptible	Good
Somerset Redstreak	Resistant	Susceptible	Good
Yarlington Mill	Susceptible	Slightly susceptible	Good

4.2 New cider apple selections from LARS

The following newly named cider apple cultivars have been selected from the extensive growers' trials of the seedlings produced from the breeding programme initiated at Long Ashton Research Station in the 1980s. They are all early maturing, ready for harvesting before the main season in mid October. All have good tree shape, regular cropping records with good sized fruit and freedom from major faults. Some are partial tip-bearers.

The following tables express their vigour as; 2 = weak, 3 = moderately vigorous and 4 = strong. Tree score is derived from assessments made on several grower trials of tree habit and suitability for bush orchards.

New cider cultivar 'Nicky' fruit falling in mid September.

Bittersweet selections: Medium – high tannin and low acidity

Name	Maturity	Flowering	Vigour	Tree score
Amelia	Late Sept- early Oct.	Mid May	2.5	1.4
Amanda	Mid-late September	Early May	3.5	3.0
Prince William	Late Sept-early Oct	Early May	2.5	1.0
Jenny	Early September	Early May	2.5	1.2
Hastings	Mid September	Mid May	3.0	3.0
Helens Apple	Late Sept-early Oct	Early May	3.5	2.8
Three Counties	Mid-late September	Early May	3.0	2.0
Jane	Late September	Mid May	2.5	1.8
Tina	Early-mid September	Early May	2.0	0.2
Connie	Mid September	Early May	4.0	0.2
Early Bird	Very early September	Early May	4.0	1.4
Lizzy	Mid September	Early May	3.0	1.2

Mild Bittersweet: Low – medium tannin and low acidity

Name	Maturity	Flowering	Vigour	Tree score
Vicky	Mid September	Early May	3.5	2.2
Naomi	Mid-late September	Late April	4.0	2.2
Nicky	Early-mid September	Late April	3.0	1.4

Bittersharp: High tannin and high acidity

Name	Maturity	Flowering	Vigour	Tree score
Joanna	Mid September	Early May	3.5	1.0
Maggie	Early September	Late April	3.0	0.1
Hannah	Mid-late September	Early May	3.0	1.0
Willy	Mid-late September	Early May	3.0	1.0
Gilly	Mid September	Mid May	3.0	3.0
Jean	Mid-late September	Mid May	3.0	0.2
Angela	Late September-early Oct	Mid May	2.5	1.8
Sally	Mid September	End April	3.5	1.4

Juicing Apples: Low tannin, sharp or sweet with high acidity

Name	Maturity	Flowering	Vigour	Tree score
Tracey	Late September	End April	2.0	1.6
Eleni	Mid September	Early May	3.0	0.2
Betty	Mid-late September	Mid May	3.0	2.6
Fiona	Early-mid September	Mid May	2.5	2.6
Debbie	Early-mid September	Mid May	3.0	2.8
Shamrock	Mid-late September	Late April	3.5	2.0

4.3 Rootstock

Cider apple cultivars grown on their own roots are generally too vigorous and cropping is delayed. For intensive bush orchards, the scion cultivar is budded onto a semi-dwarfing rootstock which gives greater uniformity of tree growth and habit, greater precocity and improved cropping. The rootstock is the most important factor in containing trees within their predicted size, but the choice depends on the site, the scion cultivar and the intended planting density. The influence on the tree of the four most often used rootstocks is described below.

MM106

This is the most commonly used semi-dwarfing rootstock, imparting moderate vigour ultimately to form a 4 – 6 m tree. It is fairly susceptible to crown and collar rot caused by the fungi *Phytophthora* , is not suitable for sites subject to periodic water-logging or prolonged winter wet. MM106 is sensitive to soil moisture, tree vigour is reduced on dry, sandy soils.

M26

This is also semi-dwarfing and produces a smaller tree than MM106 with less vigour, but which is inclined to crop most precociously. It is not resistant to collar rot and not suitable for wet soils. M26 is not suitable for weak cultivars (e.g. Dabinett) and requires a stake for a prolonged period. The union between M26 and certain cultivars (e.g. Browns Apple) is weak and has a tendency to snap under heavy crops..

MM111

This is a vigorous stock with a strong root system producing a larger tree than MM106. It is tolerant of drought and suitable for difficult or windy sites, areas that might be periodically wet, heavy soils or land where the soil depth is restricted by subsoil or water table. MM111 is less susceptible to collar and crown rot than MM106.

M25

This is the most vigorous stock and is commonly used for standard trees. It produces the largest, most robust trees for difficult conditions, but is not suitable for vigorous varieties such as Major and Ellis Bitter.

M116

This relatively recent rootstock produces a tree similar to or slightly smaller than MM106. it has good resistance to collar rot, mildew, woolly aphid and apple replant disease (ARD in the UK). Its precocity of flowering and cropping is similar to MM106. However, this rootstock has proved hard to propagate and is consequently more expensive.

Tree vigour in response to soil, rootstock and cultivar.

Tree vigour	Strong	Moderate	Weak
Soil	Strong	Average	Average
	Grade I	Grade II	Good grade III
Rootstock	MM111	MM106	M26
	M25		
Cultivar	Ellis Bitter	Somerset Redstreak	Ashton Bitter
	Major	Yarlington Mill	Dabinett
	Browns Apple	White Jersey	Harry Masters Jersey
	Kingston Black	Michelin	Chisel Jersey

4.4 Planting distance, tree density

Relatively small trees on semi-dwarfing rootstocks may be planted intensively in rows, up to 750 trees/hectare (300 trees per acre) . The distance between the rows is dictated by the machines necessary for tree management, and is normally 5.5 metres minimum to allow around 2 metres clear machinery access in the alleyways, and for good light penetration, essential for maximum cropping. The chosen apple cultivar will be influenced by the site, soil and rootstock, therefore tree growth may be manipulated by distance between the trees in the rows.

- Vigorous cultivars (e.g. Ellis Bitter), and vigorous cultivar/rootstock combinations naturally form a large tree; the distance between the trees in the rows should not be less than 3 metres, giving planting densities up to 625/hectare (250 trees/acre)

- Moderately vigorous varieties (e.g. Somerset Redstreak and combinations with moderate vigour), may be planted from 2 – 2.5 metres apart in the rows giving a density of 575 – 750/hectare (230 to over 300 trees/acre)

- Weak cultivars and combinations may be planted more intensely at 2 metres

Planting density	Cultivar/rootstock combination	Distance between trees in rows
200-240	Strong	3 metres (10′)
	Weak - moderate	2.5 – 3 m (8 – 10′)
240 - 300	Strong combinations not appropriate	-
	Weak - moderate	2 – 3 m (6 – 10′)
300 +	Weak - moderate	> 3m (10′)
600	Using interstems/interstocks	1.5m (5′)

4.4.1 Calculating how many trees are required

Number of trees/ha = $\dfrac{10000 \text{ (no. square m in a hectare)}}{\text{row width x distance in row (m)}}$

Number of trees /acre = $\dfrac{43560 \text{ (no. square feet in an acre)}}{\text{row width x distance in row (ft)}}$

NB When calculating the number of trees required, deduct 12% to allow for non-planted land around the headlands and access areas.

For traditional orchard planting of standard trees, these normally require from 30 – 35ft spacing either in rows or on the diagonal.

Planting distances (feet) and tree densities

Spacing	Trees/acre	Spacing	Trees/acre
16 x 9	303	18 x 10	242
16 x 10	272	20 x 8	272
18 x 8	303	20 x 9	242
18 x 9	269	20 x 10	218

Planting distances (metres) and tree densities

Spacing	Trees/ha	Spacing	Trees/Ha
5 x 2.75	727	5.5 x 3	606
5 x 3	666	6 x 2.5	666
5.5 x 2.5	727	6 x 2.75	606
5.5 x 2.75	661	6 x 3	555

4.4.2 Increasing intensification

By increasing the planting density the early crops harvested per hectare/acre will be increased, thus giving more rapid returns. This system lends itself to increased mechanisation of management.

If the planting distance is reduced, say, to 4.5m between rows and 1.5m within the rows, this requires around 1480 trees/ha (580 trees/acre).

The best support for close planting is provided by a post and wire system; a post every 9 or 10 trees and a wire strained along the rows to which the trees are tied at about 1m

Strong varieties and rootstocks are unsuitable for close planting.

Use of interstocks and interstems to control growth

Tree growth needs to be easily controlled for close planting. A combination of a strong rootstock to give good anchorage and tolerance of soil conditions, and an interstock or interstem inserted below the scion to reduce tree vigour, will form a suitable base for most varieties for intensive planting.

- Rootstocks M25, MM111 will provide strong roots. M116 and MM106 will give a less vigorous alternative
- M9 has proved a suitable dwarfing interstock.
- Spur Delicious has proved a suitable choice of interstem
- The interstock or stem should be high worked on the rootstock.
- The interstock or interstem needs to be at least 15cm to exert a sufficient influence in controlling the growth of the variety.

4.5 Tree quality and health

To look forward to rapid development into production, it is important to start with good quality, healthy maiden trees from a reputable source. Poor quality, miss-shaped or scantily feathered trees will always lag behind well-produced trees and require more effort to correct their problems during initial training. Always choose virus-free scions high-worked onto certified stocks and, if possible, inspect the quality of your trees at the nursery while they are still in growth.

- Trees should be pest and disease free (canker, scab and mildew etc)
- Rootstocks should be well grown, uniform sized, first year trees, sturdy enough for high-worked budding at about 30 cm.
- Rootstock M26 is not suitable for high working
- High working creates vigorous maiden trees (minimum height 120 cm), strong enough to carry numerous feathers (7 – 12) at a suitable height, that will form the first fruiting branches
- The union between the rootstock and the scion should be straight. Any bend in the tree above ground will reduce its vigour and slow its development
- Some varieties do not feather freely in the first season (e.g. Yarlington Mill, Browns Apple)
- Feathers should be retained when the trees are lifted, not tipped for convenience of handling
- After lifting trees in the nursery, the exposed roots should not be allowed to dry out. Cover trees tightly with waterproof sheeting to protect from drying winds, and damp down the roots if they begin to dry
- If there is to be a prolonged wait between lifting and planting, consider heeling-in the bundles of trees. The roots may be buried up to 30 cm in loose friable soil or compost or in a corner of the orchard site, but protect the tops from excessive wet and prolonged humidity which encourage the spread of disease
- Protect heeled-in trees from rodents and other animals
- Where trees are stored in buildings pending planting, ensure that the roots are kept moist/watered (soaked hessian sacking is ideal) and prevent rodent damage

- Dormant trees may be held in cold store at 4-6°C, providing the store has not recently held fruit. Ensure the roots are never allowed to dry out
- Standard trees should be worked on a strong rootstock, M25 or seedling
- They should be top worked to the rootstock/stem builder grown up to a minimum 2m (6'+) to allow the head to develop. Strong cultivars may be allowed to grow on their own stem.

CHAPTER 5

Site preparation

With any perennial crop, site preparation is the key to the future health and productivity of the crop. It is extremely difficult, and sometimes impossible, to correct potential problems ignored or mistakes made before planting. Their impact will last throughout the life of the orchard and the financial effect will continue year-on-year. Access for machinery needed during the life of the orchard needs to be established before planting. Roadways and gates should be in place as early as possible, ideally before the initial cultivation for planting starts. For heavily used roadways hardcore bases are essential.

5.1 Drainage

It is essential to plan and install an effective and adequate drainage system well before planting commences. The long-term viability of the orchard will be compromised by any un-addressed drainage problems and the initial outlay of installation of a drainage system will be a sound investment. Attempts to correct drainage after planting are usually far less effective and are likely to cause significant damage to the trees' established root systems.

- Seek professional help in designing the system most appropriate to the site

- The site should be thoroughly surveyed before the system is designed. This should be done well in advance of the planned planting date. Two years should give time for all planning and preparation

- Take account of experience of previous cropping and any previous drainage problems

- Take account of windbreak/hedgerow or specimen trees in or around the site which may cause blockage of drains at a later stage

- Grants may be available towards the cost of the drainage scheme

- The drainage system must be designed to take account of the planned orchard layout

- To allow for any soil damage to be made good and for final site preparation to be thoroughly undertaken, ensure that the drainage system is installed well before the planned planting time

- Ensure that all receiving ditches and drains associated with the planned system are in good order and have adequate capacity to deal with the outflow from the site

- Back-filling for piped systems is expensive, but if done properly, is an excellent investment.

5.2 Soil fertility

The basic soil fertility of the site will be dependent on the previous cropping and must be adjusted to provide the ideal nutrient status for apple growing. Certain nutrients are not very mobile in the soil. These therefore need to be applied and incorporated before planting because deficiencies cannot readily be corrected after the trees are planted. Soil pH must be corrected before planting by applying and incorporating lime. Sites that have been long-term grassland or leys, even if few or no fertilisers have been applied, are likely to have very high intrinsic fertility due to excellent soil structure. Base fertiliser rates may need to be reduced to compensate for this. Although rapid establishment is needed, if growth is excessive, vigour and cropping will be very difficult to control in later years.

- Have the soil analysed for major and minor nutrients and pH before any ground operations are carried out
- Take samples from both the upper profile (0-15 cm) and the middle profile (15-30 cm)
- On the basis of the analyses results, plan application of any necessary base fertiliser and lime during the soil cultivation process
- Ensure recommended fertilisers and lime are worked into the soil adequately before planting.

5.3 Fencing

It is vital to keep wild animals and stock out of young bush orchards to avoid damage to the trees. Tree guards, if correctly positioned, should prevent damage by rabbits and hares on young trees, but mesh fencing around the whole orchard is a better long-term solution, although it is more expensive on small sites. Damage by deer can be devastating and, for high risk sites, must be prevented by installation of deer proof fences before planting. Deer fences of well over 2m high will be needed to exclude the larger species.

- Plan fencing according to the known and expected risks from wild animals
- Maintain stock-proof boundaries to avoid damage by stray stock
- Remember any fencing or boundary must be complete around the whole orchard. Access to the orchard must be appropriately gated and animal-proof
- Fencing must not block public rights of way. Ensure appropriate stiles and gates are installed
- After fencing check the enclosed site is free from rabbits and hares, and clear site of any enclosed animals if needed
- Fencing to prevent rabbit entry needs to include a continuous fine wire mesh (usually 25mm mesh) about 90 cm above ground and buried at least 20cm in the ground to prevent burrowing

- To prevent fence damage by badgers, install badger gates where needed on their runs.

5.4 Windbreaks

Cider apple trees are subject to wind damage throughout their life, with young trees being particularly susceptible to exposure to strong winds. Windbreaks will reduce the amount of damage to the roots and anchorage, minimise damage to branches carrying heavy crops, encourage more shoot growth, enable easier training of strong centre-leader trees and will provide shelter to allow increased activity of pollinating insects. Windbreaks are particularly important on exposed south-west facing sites.

- The need for windbreaks should be considered from the earliest planning stage
- Because shelter is particularly essential for young trees, it is important to establish the windbreak well before planting, two years is ideal
- Make full use of existing hedges and shelter, supplementing as needed to fill gaps
- On very large or exposed sites internal windbreaks may be needed to supplement those around the circumference of the site
- Internal windbreaks in all except the most exposed sites, may not be needed once the orchard is approaching maturity and can be grubbed and replanted with cider apple trees
- Do not remove old hedges without authorisation from the local authority
- There is a wide choice of species for new windbreaks with native alder being the most suitable
- Coniferous windbreaks were once used, but these are not recommended now because they are less wind-porous and will increase turbulence on the leeward side, trapping cold air and leading to frost pockets
- Windbreaks are excluded from the LERAPs assessment for buffer zone size determination (see Section 9)
- Alder is a good choice for many sites, but is relatively slow-growing and may not reach an adequate height to protect very tall bush orchards
- Poplar is an option but has some major disadvantages; it is very quick-growing and needs more management than alder, it is susceptible to silverleaf and also in late summer may lose most of its leaf to poplar rust, it has an extensive root system and will block and damage drains
- Mature windbreaks need to be properly maintained and trimmed or topped as necessary
- Windbreaks can be made into very good reservoirs for beneficial organisms and to act as effective 'green corridors' when the under-storey is managed to encourage a diverse range of plant species below the lower branches of the trees.

5.5 Planting

Planting strong maiden trees in a well prepared site

The planting technique and method should put as little stress on the trees as possible and give them the best possible chance of rapid establishment. Trees should be fully dormant on receipt but they still need to be treated with care *and their roots must never be allowed to dry out before planting.* Although site preparation and planning for planting may have been meticulous, careless handling of the trees after receipt from the nursery and the planting process itself can compromise the economic future of the orchard.

- Accurate marking-out is essential and should only be done on completion of the final cultivation and fertiliser incorporation

- On receipt of trees from the nursery protect roots from drying-out. Bare-rooted trees placed in cold store are particularly prone to drying-out

- Always handle trees carefully to avoid unnecessary damage to the roots or shoots/feathers

- If soil preparation will not be complete for some time, or ground conditions are unsuitable, heel trees in on a sheltered and guarded site, lightly firming loose soil around the roots to minimise disturbance when lifted for planting. Water in if soil is dry

- Drive stakes in to required depth before planting (see 5.6 below)

- Planting should be done in the winter when the trees are dormant. Early planting allows root growth to establish before the foliage emerges, but can cause problems if prolonged wet weather follows planting, particularly on heavy soils

- Trees should be planted on the leeward side of stakes

- Never plant in very dry soil conditions as roots will dry on contact with the soil

- Be prepared to apply water, using a bowser and hose, if unusually dry conditions follow planting, or if planting is done late

- ***Never plant in very wet conditions.*** Soil should be friable in the planting holes

- If plants have been heeled-in correctly they are better left rather than planted in poor soil conditions

- Planting holes should be large enough to contain the existing roots on the nursery trees without undue bending or twisting

Planting to the correct depth in an ideal, rough sided, hand dug hole

- When excavating holes avoid smearing the sides. Using a fork prevents this
- Aim to plant as soon as the holes are dug
- Before planting remove any badly damaged roots
- When machine planting ensure the correct depth setting is used
- The union between the rootstock and scion (cultivar) must be at least 15cm above the final soil level to prevent direct scion rooting. M26 should be at ground level

Bad Planting. An ineffective stake, weak tie and a plastic rabbit guard; result windrock, lodging and ultimately, death of the tree.

- After placing the tree in the planting hole, re-fill with crumbly/friable soil and **lightly but firmly** compress the soil over the roots all the way around the tree, topping up the soil to the correct depth (proud of the soil surface to allow settling and to prevent puddling around the tree)

- Compressing must be light on wet soils and those prone to capping or panning. More pressure may be needed on drier and more open soils

- Immediately after planting, secure the tree to the stake

- After tying prune out (or back) any badly damaged shoots/feathers

- Organic mulches such as straw or well-rotted FYM, applied around each tree will help conserve moisture, speed establishment and reduce weed problems

- Where mulches are used, leave a small un-mulched circle around the trunk to minimise disease and small vermin problems.

5.6 Staking, tying and tree guards

Having got this far some attention to detail is needed to ensure that the trees are not subject to damage due to wind-rock or rabbit/hare grazing damage.

A good, wire perimeter fence, buried and with a top wire, is often more economical in a large field than individual rabbit guards.

- When planting by hand or auger stakes must be inserted before planting

- Stake size and depth will be determined by the rootstock/cultivar combination and soil type and depth

- Stakes need to be treated with a wood preservative to ensure they last right through the establishment period
- Ensure stakes are vertical and correctly positioned a foot's width from the base of the trunk
- In later years once trees are well anchored, stakes may need to be removed to facilitate shaking
- Immediately after planting, trees must be tied to their stakes
- Ties should be placed below the lowest shoot/feather and within about 2cm of the top of the stake to prevent rubbing
- Ties must allow space of at least 10cm between the tree and the stake to prevent rubbing damage
- Ties secured to the trunk must allow for expansion of the trunk diameter
- The tie should be tightly secured to the stake to reduce slipping
- Ties need to be checked regularly, ensuring that they are in place and not too tight around the trunk. If ties are allowed to cut into the bark this can result in serious canker problems or death of the tree
- If the site is not securely fenced against rabbits and hares, young trees will need to be protected by individual trunk guards immediately after planting
- Rabbits and hares can still cause damage to quite large trees of some varieties
- Guards need to be high enough to protect against rabbits standing on their hind legs to feed
- Guards must allow for trunk expansion and be regularly adjusted or replaced
- One potential disadvantage of tree guards is that some of the lower feathers of the nursery tree may need to be removed which will slow development to full cropping
- Spiral plastic guards are cheap and easy to apply but are only suitable on very young trees and are best avoided since they tend to keep the trunk wet for longer periods and can increase disease (canker/collar rot) risk
- Wire mesh guards are a good choice, but are more labour intensive to fit initially and are easily deformed by tree shakers
- Use 25 x 25 mm mesh wire for guards
- Wrap around perforated plastic guards are preferred. These expand with the tree as the trunk grows and are less likely to be damaged by tree shakers.

5.6.1 Using posts and wire as an alternative tree support method

This method requires stronger stakes inserted between every 5 – 10 trees depending on planting density and rootstock/cultivar combination. Trees are tied with light weight tubular plastic tree ties to a high tensile kinked wire strained between the stakes on the windward side at about 1.25m. This system makes considerable saving on initial cost of stakes and allows free access to the tree trunks for shaking at harvesting, however access across the rows is inhibited.

Wrap-around rabbit guards protect trees in a post and wire planting.

5.6.2 Staking standard trees

- Standard trees require heavy duty stakes inserted at least 50cm into the ground.

- The stake should not extend above the first lateral branches.

- Trees should be tied with heavy duty material nailed close to the top of the stake and separated from the tree with a block to prevent rubbing.

- Sturdy guards suitable to protect against the planned livestock should be fixed to the stake. A spiral of barbed wire wound from base to top of the guard is an excellent deterrent against livestock rubbing.

5.7 Alleys

Alleyways are a fundamental part of the orchard and must be established well before regular mechanical operations are needed in the early stages of the orchard. The composition of the alleyways must take account of the need to carry regular traffic of heavy machines, mechanical fruit collection and the effect of heavy shading later in the orchards life. Creating alleyways from an original sward or using the 'tumbledown' method following cultivation is not advisable as the grass composition is unlikely to be suitable.

- Planting can be done into a ley specifically sown for orchard alleys. Such leys are not ideal for silage

- To avoid competition for water, apply herbicide to the ley along the tree rows prior to or soon after planting

- It is easier to establish a new sward in September, then apply herbicide after marking out

- Trees may be planted into bare soil and the sward established at a later stage by seeding the alleyways only.

- Inter-cropping up the alleyways in young orchards is likely to compromise some essential operations needed on the trees and is best avoided

- Inter-cropping will delay the establishment of a suitable alleyway sward and can lead to increased compaction and rutting problems later

- Alleyways must be wide enough to cover the widest wheelbase of equipment likely to be used in the orchard

- If possible during site preparation (pre-planting), minimise the amount of base fertiliser applied to the future alleyways

- Although bio-diversity will be enhanced by using a mix of grass and herbaceous plants in the alleyway, grass needs to be the main constituent of the alley sward to ensure it has the necessary characteristics

- The alley sward needs to have the following main characteristics: -

  Quick and easy establishment

  Good wear tolerance

  An even surface

  A dense structure which will be resistant to invasive weed incursion (including other grasses)

  Provide good surface for machinery traction

  Low vigour to reduce the number of mowings needed each season

  Good recovery ability after heavy traffic or prolonged adverse weather

- Choice of sward composition will depend on the soil type and to some extent the climate and topography

- Various combinations of fescue, bent and perennial ryegrass may be used, but in order to establish the most appropriate sward for your site seek professional advice

- Germination and establishment is best from sowings made in March, April or September. For fescue mixes sow in September for best results

- To minimise future problems with rutting, make sure that the soil in the alleyways has been consolidated and is firm after sowing.

CHAPTER 6

Crop husbandry

6.1 Pruning

Annual cropping Dabinett. i) last year's vegetative growth; ii) 2 year old wood with some well developed flower buds; iii) 3 year old wood; an ideal mixture of established spurs; some about to flower, and some resting.

6.1.1 Pruning in the formative years

Intensive cider apple trees are best grown to a centre leader shape; a main vertical trunk bearing many lightweight, more or less horizontal, lateral branches evenly distributed throughout its height. It is essential that each tree fills its allotted space rapidly, ultimately forming an 'A' shaped hedgerow canopy along the rows. This tree shape allows the most effective use of the light energy source for growth, flower and crop production.

- Pruning is normally carried out during the dormant season, after leaf-fall, from November onwards

- To maintain a strong centre leader, the trunk must continue with a gentle taper from bottom to the apex, without any noticeable bottlenecks which indicate a check to its growth

- Bottlenecks are caused by too many lateral branches arising from a limited section of the main trunk. As a guide, the distance of a hands-breadth at the trunk should be left between laterals in young trees

- Always remove whole branches from back at the trunk. Do not be tempted to cut back part of branches

3 year old Dabinett already cropping but maintaining steady growth in the leader which has been kept clear of competitive shoots.

- Remove superfluous branches as soon as possible on weaker cultivars
- Selection and prompt thinning of upright branches arising low down in some cultivars, (e.g. Michelin and Browns Apple) will avoid the formation of a multi-leader tree which may subsequently need heavy remedial pruning
- Remove those branches which will extend into the alleyway in preference to those within the rows
- Remove any dense layered branches, aiming for evenly spaced and distributed branches that fill the tree space and efficiently intercept the light
- Remove shoots arising near the top of the tree that are in competition with the leader. This should be done on weaker varieties during the growing season, but can be left later on stronger varieties, since it will help to slow growth and produce better branch angles below
- On weakly growing trees and less vigorous cultivars likely to loose the leader, prune the leading shoot back to a bud on the windward side in the dormant season. Prune by ⅓ to ½, harder for weaker growth. Most strong growing varieties may not require this treatment

6.1.2 Manipulating cropping in the formative years

It is essential that the centre leader maintains its vigour during the early years in order for the tree to reach its mature height quickly. Upright branches tend to be more vigorous, but as branch angles move towards the horizontal, leafy, vegetative vigour is replaced with a tendency to form flower buds. Pruning and training during this stage aims at manipulating leafy vigour to achieve a balance between the start of cropping and the continued healthy vegetative development of the tree framework. Too much vegetative growth will delay flower bud formation and fruit set, but too much fruit from early crops will limit the size of the tree, the efficiency of its light interception and hence, subsequent crops. This may result in the early onset of a biennial cropping pattern.

- In many cases, many of the more upright-growing branches will be brought down naturally to an acceptable angle and held there by the weight of the first crop of fruit. Certain cultivars (e.g. Michelin) where this does not occur naturally, may need help by twisting of some branches to the horizontal. If this is done in the late summer, from August to September, the natural stiffness of the woody tissue, helped by the weight of any fruit, should hold the branch permanently in position. There are more expensive alternative methods involving weighting or tying down branches with strings to stakes.

2 year old Michelin in a generous weed-free strip with the remains of a straw mulch laid to conserve moisture in their unusually dry, first year.

Young Major with well-spaced, horizontal branches and a strong, gently tapering, central trunk and leader shoot.

- Prune the weakest trees first, soon after leaf-fall, from November onwards
- Vigorous trees may be pruned latest, even after bud-break, to help control vegetative growth
- To assist vigorous cultivars to form flower bud, avoid heavy pruning during the dormant season, since this stimulates vegetative growth. Minimal pruning allows competition between branches to slow vegetative growth naturally, and flower bud will be formed
- Vigorous pruning in the dormant season can usefully stimulate growth in weaker trees and less vigorous cultivars
- Summer pruning slows down vegetative growth and helps the formation of flower bud
- Reducing the width of the bare herbicide strip will increase the competition between the grass sward and tree roots. This helps to moderate vigour in difficult to control young trees.

6.1.3 Pruning mature trees

An 'A' shaped hedgerow canopy along the tree rows allows maximum light interception, the trees' energy source, to keep leaves healthy and efficient, and fruit crops good and regular. To maintain this, old branches need to be removed as they become unproductive. This allows light to penetrate into the canopy, promoting the replacement of old wood by new shoots with strong spurs and buds. Regular pruning also improves air circulation and spray penetration, which helps to minimise diseases such as scab. Once trees have achieved their natural height, dense growth on the tops needs thinning to prevent it overshadowing the canopy below, with a consequent decline in bud strength and cropping.

- Pruning is normally carried out in the dormant season after leaf-fall, from November onwards
- The pruning operation is much easier if it is carried out regularly and before the branches and foliage get too dense. Prune at least every third year
- Always remove whole branches from back at the trunk. Do not be tempted to cut back part of branches
- Remove large diameter old branches, broken, diseased or crossing branches, and those which are layered over other branches and obscure light penetration
- Work to maximise light penetration to all lateral branches and to those new shoots on the trunk which will ultimately form replacement branches
- Maintain a strong centre leader by removing competing shoots and branches
- As the tree matures the trunk must still continue with a gentle taper from bottom to the apex. Remove lateral branches from noticeable bottlenecks which indicate a check to the leader's growth

Mature Dabinett with a good, strong centre leader. The light-weight, horizontal, cropping branches require only light annual pruning

- Thin out the tops of trees if they overshadow the canopy below. This job may also be done in the growing season
- Dropping the pruned branches into alternate rows facilitates the clearing job after pruning is finished and leaves every other alleyway open for early spray access in the spring.

6.1.4 Mechanical shaping as a pruning management aid

With the aim of reducing pruning costs and time, also improving access for machinery, trees may be cut back hard by machine, preferably with a reciprocating blade rather than a flail cutter or spinning disc, to remove a third of branch length into 2 and 3 year old wood

- A reciprocating blade makes a cleaner job with less torn branches and damaged wood
- Mechanical pruning is not a complete replacement for hand pruning
- A follow-up 'tidying' by hand will be needed, as will a detailed hand pruning every 3 – 4 years to remove larger branches
- If the operation is well timed it improves light penetration to the centre of the tree, stimulating minimal shoot growth but encouraging new and stronger fruit buds on older wood
- There may be some initial reduction in fruit crop but better fruit set should compensate for this in subsequent years
- Spray penetration is improved, more reaching the centre of the tree from the spray that is normally intercepted by the lower branches in the alleyway.
- Air movement through the tree canopy should also be improved, hopefully making the microclimate less conducive to scab.
- Not all varieties are suitable candidates for mechanical pruning, such as very vigorous or upright cultivars or those prone to silverleaf infection.

Timing of operation

- It should be remembered that any pruning or trimming in winter will invigorate, stimulating new tree growth the following season, much of which may be unwanted
- Preliminary pruning in winter will usually need a follow-up summer pruning
- Growth stimulation is minimal if the pruning is done during the growing season between June and August, ideally at around the longest day
- This applies especially to the cutting back of the tops of mature trees (topping). To be successful, topping should be done during the summer period (June – August) even though extrication and removal of the lopped material may be difficult.
- Topping in the dormant season will cause considerable leafy regrowth and is bound to be counter productive.

Negative aspect of mechanical pruning

Prunings left in the alleyways after summer trimming cause serious problems during the fruit processing at the factory where they block pipelines and halt processing. Small twigs can remain a hazard even after chopping or pulverising. Pulverize slowly to be successful. Heavier prunings need to be collected and removed prior to harvesting fruit.

Mechanical shaping; before and after in July

Minimal regrowth after summer pruning

6.2 Alley maintenance

Orchard swards need to be tough, resilient and extremely wear tolerant to be able to carry heavy machinery at harvesting time and withstand passes by a sprayer, often in wet conditions in spring. The sward needs to be able to repair itself quickly after winter damage, without weed incursion. Wheel ruts need to be eliminated prior to machine harvesting. All of this needs annual maintenance, but careful management of the sward will also benefit the trees by improving soil structure which aids drainage and root penetration.

Grass can be very competitive for nutrients and water, which can have a profound effect on growth and cropping, especially of young trees (See section 6.4). This competition eases with tree maturity when the grass can be extended further under the trees. However the grass will still be in competition with the trees for nutrients especially nitrogen. Fruit harvested from the grass is usually much cleaner than that harvested from bare soil.

Various intercrops have been tried in bush orchards but most have serious disadvantages, such as impeding access to the trees when they require spraying, creating a residual weed problem, or leaving behind uneven ground which is difficult and expensive to rectify with the trees in place. On a good site it is possible to take a silage crop off a purpose-sown ley for the first few years without harm, providing an adequate herbicide strip is maintained. Re-seeding will be needed to establish the correct permanent alleyway.

Summer maintenance

- Keep the grass between 5–10 cm during the summer. Newly-sown grass needs more frequent mowing to encourage tillering for a dense sward

- Do not let the grass get too long before mowing, since heavy grass cuttings will rot and cause bare patches in the sward, but avoid unnecessary mowing which is expensive and energy inefficient

- Spot treat troublesome perennial weeds like thistles, nettles, docks and buttercup which will create bare patches and smother useful grass and flower species

- Aerate the sward frequently with a spiked tine roller to improve surface drainage and encourage rooting.

- If grass growth is very poor, apply a low nitrate compound fertilizer (10:15:10 at 0.25 tonnes/ha) after spiking. Too much nitrate encourages excessive grass growth. A slow growing sward saves mowing and encourages flowering species which are useful to beneficial insects

- When heavy machinery has to be used in wet conditions, low pressure tyres help to distribute weight and minimise rutting

- Once trees have reached maturity and are cropping well and regularly, it is possible to reduce the width of the herbicide strip without significant competition from the grass. To aid machine harvesting, late summer growth of the grass margin (the outside 30 cm) may be retarded with an appropriate herbicide spray applied at a low rate by the end of June.

A good sward of fine, non-competitive grasses is allowed to grow close to the tree trunks but retarded with a low-rate herbicide in June to facilitate fruit harvest.

Winter and spring sward renovation

- If possible, aerate the sward with a spiked tine roller after harvesting to improve surface drainage and encourage rooting

- Before winter, check land-drain outlets to make sure that they are running freely and that the ditches are clear

- If the land-drains were properly backfilled, occasional passes with a mole plough along the alleyway in suitable conditions (needs to be moist, but not saturated), will help to reconnect drains in heavy, clayey soils. This should not be done if there is no backfill, since it will increase drainage problems

- Where heavy compaction has occurred, one or more passes with a sub-soil plough will help to loosen and improve soil structure. This must be done in dry conditions and an exploratory pit dug under the sward will help to judge if the soil is dry enough at plough level for it to shatter adequately

- Once conditions begin to dry in the spring, the worst wheel ruts can be rolled lightly and the grass and thatch can be lifted with a harrow prior to the first cut

- Where a power harrow is used to correct heavy rutting, re-seeding with a ryegrass/fescue renovation mixture in spring may be needed.

6.3 Nutrition

The major nutrients, potash (K), phosphate (P) and magnesium (Mg), should be applied pre-planting and the pH adjusted according to soil analysis. Normally no further fertilizers will need to be applied for the next 3 years while the trees' roots are exploring a limited area. Nutrients then need to be replaced as they are depleted from the soil by the growing trees and after crops are removed. In order to check that sufficient but not excessive amounts are being replaced, nutrient levels need to be monitored by regular soil analysis. As the orchard matures, leaf analysis gives a further indication of how nutrients are utilised by the trees. Older trees may have difficulty in getting their full nutrient requirement (especially minor nutrients such as boron and trace elements) which may need to be supplemented by foliar feeding.

- After pre-planting correction of soil phosphate, potash and magnesium levels, no further soil amendments should be needed for the first 3 years of an orchard

- Fertilizer requirements are normally quoted as the amount needed per hectare. To avoid wasting fertilizer, this is only applied to the herbicide strip in the tree rows, the area most occupied by tree roots. See Appendix V for how to calculate the area of the herbicide strip for band-spreading

- Regular soil sampling for nutrient analysis will guard against wasting fertilizer with unnecessary routine applications, and prevent levels of available nutrients from getting too low. Sample during the dormant season every 3 years unless problems arise

- Fertilizer amendments should normally be applied in the spring, according to requirements indicated, expressed as units/acre, kg/ha or indices (see table below)

- If on analysis, a major nutrient index is 1 or over, the annual requirement may be applied at twice the recommended rate, every second year

- Nutrient deficiencies may often show up as characteristic leaf symptoms (see Appendix IV), indicating acute or chronic problems with nutrient availability. Leaf sampling and analysis gives an accurate diagnosis for correction.

- For older, mature trees, leaf sampling and analysis every few years gives a clearer picture of the nutrients actually getting into the tree. This can show up problems of mobility from soil to the tree, even though soil analysis might indicate nutrients to be in plentiful supply.

- Many nutrient deficiencies can be relieved by foliar sprays during the growing season.

For further information on nutrients and nutritional deficiencies go to Appendix IV.

Annual requirement for phosphate, potash and magnesium for established orchards (kg/ha)

Nutrient	P, K, Mg Index			
	0	1	2	3 and over
Phosphate (P₂O₅)	80	40	20	Nil
Potash (K₂O)	220	150	80	Nil
Magnesium (Mg)	60	40	30	Nil

(To convert to units per acre, multiply the kg/ha figures by 0.8.)

Nitrate

The nitrate (N) recommendations of 60 – 120 kg/ha, should be taken as a guide only. The actual requirement depends very much on local conditions; soil type and depth, variety, rootstock, cropping pattern, tree spacing and pruning. The amount needed can best be judged by the seasonal growth of shoots and their leaf colour. The aim is to maintain a balance between shoot growth, high yields of quality fruit and a continuity of fruit bud initiation from year to year.

- Established cider orchards may use from 60 – 120 kg/ha of nitrate per year. A rate towards the top limit may be needed in wet seasons, but lower rates within the guidelines will be sufficient for non-cropping or very vigorous trees

- Nitrogen applied as nitrate, is very soluble and easily leached out of the soil by rain. To minimise this risk and for maximum benefit to the trees, nitrate is best supplied in two or more applications, half in the spring for flowering, fruit-set and extension growth, and the remainder in late July or August to aid bud formation

- Young trees under 3 years are able to exploit naturally occurring nitrates and need no additional application which will encourage vigorous shoot growth without initiating fruit bud

- Nitrate fertilizers evaporate easily on the soil surface. Time applications to precede rainfall, so that they are quickly washed down to the root zone and utilised efficiently.

Soil pH

The pH is a measure of the acidity or alkalinity of the soil and should be at an optimum of pH 6.5 for apple trees (pH 7 is neutral). Much above or below this, many nutrients in the soil become increasingly locked up and unavailable for uptake by the tree roots. This will eventually lead to nutrient deficiencies and a decline in tree performance. Some elements become more available, leading to toxicity symptoms. The pH tends to fall (become more acidic) in the root zone under the herbicide strip. This needs periodic correction by spreading lime to raise the pH to 6.5.

- Mature trees are tolerant of slightly acidic conditions pH 6.0 – 6.5 but newly planted trees are more sensitive and require a pH at 6.5
- Measurement of pH is quick, easy and inexpensive to have done
- A lime application may take some time to correct the pH, especially if the soil has been allowed to get acidic (below pH 5.5)
- For smooth nutrient availability and regular cropping, it is advisable to apply lime before the pH drops too far
- Where magnesium levels and pH need simultaneous correction, ground magnesium limestone can accomplish both requirements with one application.

6.4 Growth control

Bush trees need to be brought into cropping as soon as possible in order to recoup the considerable capital outlay in planting an orchard. At the same time, the tree framework needs to be established quickly to form the centre-leader dominant, A-shaped hedgerow for maximum and prolonged fruit production. This requires a delicate balance to be maintained between vigorous, vegetative shoot and leaf growth, and the formation of fruiting spurs and flower buds; two aspects of growth which are in direct competition. Tailor your growth control policy for each orchard to balance the need to control vigour, to maximise yield and to avoid biennialism. This balance may be adjusted by several means. Pruning is the best way of controlling vegetative growth, but branch manipulation and the prudent use of approved chemicals for growth control can be extremely effective.

- Winter pruning tends to invigorate tree growth but pruning carried out after shoot growth has started, will reduce vigour or even stop re-growth.

- Winter pruning which is carried out in the later part of the dormant season will tend to have a greater effect on controlling vigour. It is best to prune the weakest trees first and leave the strongest to be pruned in early spring.

- Vigorously growing trees are best controlled with minimal pruning. Heavy pruning will tend to invigorate them further and encourage many new shoots.

- For young orchards, branch bending can be used to create the ideal tree framework. Upwardly growing branches will grow vigorously and vegetatively. The nearer the branch angle is to horizontal, the weaker the growth will become, and the branch more inclined to produce flowering spurs and hold fruit.

- Two to three year old branches bent down to a more horizontal angle in August when the wood is beginning to stiffen should stay in position, but if this is done too soon, the end of the branch will grow upwards again.

- Sward grasses and weeds are highly competitive with young trees. Strongly growing trees may be kept in check by allowing the grass to reduce the width of the herbicide strip. Conversely, a wider bare strip will remove all competition from weakly growing trees.

- On young trees appropriate hand-thinning of blossom or fruitlets, although not economic for that particular year, will significantly reduce the risk of biennial bearing and may be justified in terms of the long-term productivity of the orchard

- Consider the use of an approved chemical treatment for growth control and fruit set (e.g. Cultar, Regalis etc.), but seek advice on the most appropriate rates and timing of application for each orchard

- Avoid excessive use of fertilisers (see Section 6.3).

6.5 Maintenance of drains

Having ensured that the orchard site was prepared correctly before planting, it is essential to maintain all ditches and drains in good working order throughout the life of the orchard. Even well established orchards are not immune to the effect of poor or deteriorating soil drainage.

Late summer dry soil conditions ideal for sub-soiling to relieve compaction and improve winter drainage on heavy soils.

- Keep all ditches clear of blockages and excavate regularly as needed, preferably under relatively dry conditions, to maintain their optimum profile

- Check regularly for evidence of blocked or collapsed drains

- Excavate and repair drains promptly when a problem is identified

- Consider the use of sub-soiling to supplement drainage and to improve the soil structure
- Sub-soiling is best done when the soil is reasonably, but not excessively, dry
- Late summer/early autumn usually provides the best conditions for sub-soiling, *but* care must be taken not to damage roots if done before harvest, nor to leave an uneven surface which will hinder mechanical fruit collection
- Do not sub-soil too close to the trees where root damage may occur.

6.6 Grazing policy

Grazing is an alternative method of control of grass within the orchard, but is only suitable for standard orchards where the crop canopy is sufficiently high to be out of reach of the stock. To avoid contamination of harvested fruit with animal waste and the associated disease risks, grazing must stop well before harvest.

- As stock can seriously damage young trees and affect future cropping, it is essential to guard individual trees
- Avoid 'poaching' by stock as it will damage the trees' fibrous roots and reduce both crop and the efficacy of mechanical fruit collection
- Ensure that fences and hedges around orchards are stock-proof
- Avoid over-grazing
- Remove stock from orchard well before apples start to fall and harvest is due
- Stock removal should ideally be done 56 days before fruit collection
- Liaise with your customer about their requirements for stock removal.

6.7 Post-harvest husbandry

Heavy machinery travelling through and working in the orchard during harvest is likely to cause some damage to the ground and trees, particularly under wet conditions.

- Check tree guards, ties and stakes, and replace or repair as needed straight after harvest
- Make good any damage to the roadways, alleyways and headlands where harvesting has resulted in heavy rutting etc.
- Identify areas which will need special attention (e.g. sub-soiling in drier soil conditions)
- Tidy up any damage caused to branches and the framework of the tree as soon as possible
- Carry out winter pruning. Consider painting major cuts with an approved paint to minimise disease problems

- Remove or pulverise prunings as soon as possible
- Pulverised prunings may cause problems with mechanical fruit collection at the next harvest
- In orchards where *Nectria* canker is a problem pulverised prunings may be a source of inoculum for tree infection. If possible prunings should be removed and burnt
- Repair and maintain all orchard boundaries, particularly where deer, rabbits or hares may be a problem.

CHAPTER 7

Crop Protection

Crop protection has an impact on many other aspects of growing cider apples. Other sections in this guide include references to crop protection, particularly the application of pesticides. Safety should be the key consideration when applying control measures against pests, diseases and weeds. Any treatments needed should have the minimum possible impact on the operator, the consumer and the environment. Non-chemical methods of control should always be considered.

The key elements of successful crop protection are

- Prevention: the use of indirect methods such as site selection, varietal selection and optimal use of fertiliser
- Monitoring: regular crop checks to identify potential problems
- Prediction: using historical records to anticipate a problem, and using forecasting systems for pest and disease
- Decision-making: ensuring that the correct decision is made by using all available information and advice
- Application of controls or preventative measures.

By employing all of these elements, growers will be using the Integrated Crop Management (ICM) approach which is now demanded by many customers.

7.1 Pesticide applications, training and legislation

All operators using pesticide application equipment must have received proper training and obtained the relevant certificate of competence. Training certificates are issued by the National Proficiency Tests Council (NPTC). Different certificates are needed for the application of pesticides applied by an air-assisted sprayer and for herbicide sprayers (hydraulic sprayers). Additionally, most customers and farm assurance schemes require spray operators to be members of the National Register of Sprayer Operators (NRoSO), which is operated by the NPTC.

Where possible operators should receive training from the sprayer manufacturer, and have access to all relevant instruction books and manuals.

A wide range of legislation covers pesticide application, including health and safety and environmental issues, see Sections 9, 11 and 12.

Pesticides are only permitted to be applied to crops under the terms of the Food and Environment Protection Act 1985 (FEPA) and the Control of Pesticides Regulations 1986 (COPR), see section 7.5.

7.2 First permitted harvest date (harvest interval)

The majority of pesticide labels include a minimum harvest interval for the product. This is the minimum gap which must be left, in days or weeks, between the application of a pesticide and the harvesting of the crop. The minimum harvest interval is a statutory part of the label. It will normally ensure that the apples will be safe to consume or be processed, and that any residues of the active ingredient(s) of the product in the fruit at harvest will not exceed the Maximum Residue Level (MRL).

7.3 Pesticide application equipment and application method

Most insecticides, acaricides, fungicides and growth regulators are approved for application through air-assisted sprayers, while herbicides should be applied using a hydraulic or CDA sprayer.

- Only trained and qualified operators may apply or work with pesticides

- Sprayers must be regularly maintained according to the manufacturer's schedule and worn or damaged parts should be replaced as needed (e.g. nozzles, belts, filters)

- Sprayers must be correctly calibrated. Pressure gauges, spray tank level indicators, tractor odometers and other monitoring equipment should all be operational and accurate

- All safety devices (e.g. PTO guards, fan housings, drawbar linch pins) must be secured in place and be undamaged

- Operators must have the appropriate personal protective clothing specified for the pesticides to be applied (see pesticide label)

- Sprayers should always be washed/flushed out with clean water after use

- At the end of the season the sprayer should be drained, serviced and stored under cover

- Pesticides should always be applied in accordance with the product label

- Sprayers should be set up to apply the pesticide as evenly and accurately as possible to the target, avoiding contamination of non-target areas. Dosage and application rates must relate to the calculated sprayed ha/acre occupied by the trees

- Non-target areas must include buffer zones, identified by the user in their Local Environmental Risk Assessments for Pesticides (LERAPs)

- LERAP covers all types of pesticide

- Buffer zones identified under a LERAP must be recorded and kept with spray records

- Spray volume and dosage rates should be adjusted according to the tree size/target.

7.4 Decision making – the need for and the timing of treatment

Avoid the use of routine applications; always assess the need for treatment before making a decision.

- Refer to previous records of problems in individual orchards
- Each orchard should be assessed weekly for pest, disease and weed problems throughout the growing season
- Where available or appropriate use diagnostic test kits (e.g. for *Phytophthora*) and pest traps (e.g. for codling moth, apple sawfly etc)
- Records should be kept of the results of monitoring
- Refer to pest and disease forecasting or prediction information
- Take account of recent and forecast weather when assessing pest and disease risk (e.g. scab, mite pests)
- The level of predators and parasites present in the orchard should be taken into account when assessing the risk of pest damage
- Seek advice from a qualified consultant (ideally BASIS qualified).
- Having gathered all the relevant information and advice decide on the need for treatment

7.5 Approval of pesticides

The Food and Environment Protection Act 1985 (FEPA) and the Control of Pesticides Regulations 1986 (COPR) cover all aspects of the use of pesticides. The Chemicals Regulation Directorate (CRD), part of the Health and Safety Executive, is responsible for administering FEPA and COPR. Only approved pesticides may be stored, marketed and used in the UK. Official approval relates to specific formulations (trade names) and not just to the active ingredient. Most usage of pesticides on cider apples will be under the terms of the Full Approval, whereby all information is included on the pesticide label. There is another type of approval where certain uses in addition to those on the label are permitted. This is the Specific Off-label Approval (SOLA). The main statutory part of the label includes the following:-

- Field of use (e.g. agriculture, horticulture etc.)
- Specific crops on which usage is permitted
- Maximum individual dosage rate per hectare
- Maximum number of applications per crop (cropping year)
- Minimum interval between application and harvest
- Operator protection and training requirements.

Before applying a pesticide under a SOLA, the appropriate up-to-date SOLA notice must be obtained and kept with spray records. Notices are available, as hard or electronic copy, from DEFRA or CRD and from most pesticide suppliers or horticultural consultants (e.g. ADAS, FAST).

7.6 Invertebrate pest control

(For vertebrate pests refer to Sections 5.3 and 5.6)

There are a very large number of invertebrates which feed on apple trees. However, in many cases, the damage they cause does not affect the yield of fruit. Unlike with dessert and culinary apples, pests which purely affect fruit quality are usually of little importance in cider apple production. For many pests of apples there are very effective, naturally-occurring predators or parasites, which will, under the right conditions, reduce the pest to a level where control is not justified. Naturally-occurring beneficial organisms are often very susceptible to pesticides applied for control of pests and diseases, particularly to broad-spectrum insecticides.

Horticultural Research International (HRI)

Many beneficial insects can be "managed" to act as very effective predators in controlling orchard pests. Top Left: phytoseiid mites ("typhs"); top right: anthocorid larva attacking aphid; bottom left black-kneed capsid nymph; bottom right: larva of green lacewing

- Regular orchard monitoring for pest presence/damage must be carried out through the growing season
- Pesticides should only be applied where thresholds are exceeded (see next section)
- Pesticides should be selected to control the target species while having the minimum effect on non-target species
- To maximise yields from young orchards it is important to control any pest which will slow development of the tree framework. Certain caterpillar species, capsids and apple leaf midge are most likely to cause these problems, but moderate populations are very unlikely to need treatment on established orchards
- Pests which mainly cause early superficial fruit damage (e.g. capsids), are unlikely to need treating
- With the notable exception of apple sawfly, damage by fruit-boring pests such as codling moth, fruitlet-mining tortrix moth and dock sawfly do not have a direct effect on yield. The damage they cause may however allow development of brown rot which will reduce marketable yield and cause rapid deterioration of ripe fruit
- Always follow the pesticide label instructions.

7.6.1 Pests, thresholds, status and damage risk

Unlike for culinary and dessert apples, no detailed studies have been done to establish thresholds above which pesticide treatment would give an economic benefit in cider apple orchards. The thresholds given below, are based on field experience over many seasons for the most common pests likely to be found in cider apple orchards. Certain other pests may occur and cause damage. As a rule-of-thumb, other foliage damaging pests will need to be controlled if over 20-30% of the foliage is damaged.

Cider apples are attacked by a wide range of pest types and species and it is not practical to give details of each pest in this guide. For more detail on pest life cycles, damage caused and control strategies refer to 'The best practice guide for UK apple production' published by DEFRA.

Pest thresholds given are based on whole-orchard monitoring. Pests may be localised and when assessments are averaged over the whole orchard, treatment may not be justified. In some cases, only part of an orchard may need treating. Monitoring for pests must be done systematically on a regular basis. Ideally, 50 trees per orchard should be assessed and these should be randomly selected throughout the orchard. Refer to 'The best practice guide for UK apple production' for full details on assessment and monitoring methods.

Cider apple pest thresholds

The thresholds given below are specific to cider apples and should not necessarily be applied to dessert or culinary apples.

The thresholds given only cover the 'key pests' and 'potentially serious pests' as identified in the second table below. Treatment decisions for the pests in the 'minor' category will normally depend on the history of the pest in the individual orchard over several seasons; several of these pests are cyclical and can gradually build up over a number of seasons.

Growth stage, pest	*Threshold*
Dormant period	
Apple rust mite	20 mites per bud*
Fruit tree red spider mite, winter eggs	30% branch nodes with >5 eggs*
Bud-burst to mouse ear	
Apple rust mite	5 mites per outer rosette leaf*
Apple blossom weevil	5% capped blossoms previous season
	Beat branches, 2 weevils per 50 beats
Apple sucker	5 eggs per node
Green cluster to pink bud	
Rosy apple aphid	presence
Winter moth or tortrix moth caterpillars	10% trusses infested
Apple blossom weevil	adult weevils in 1% of trusses
Late blossom to petal fall	
Rosy apple aphid	presence
Apple sawfly	presence (if not seen this year but damage seen last year, then high risk)
Winter moth or other caterpillars	10% trusses infested
Apple rust mite	10 mites per leaf*
Petal fall onwards	
Rosy apple aphid	Young trees – presence
	Mature trees – presence until early July
Fruit tree red spider mite	2 mites per leaf*
Apple rust mite	10-50 mites per leaf, higher level later in season*

* = *if good populations of predatory mites (Typhs) are present in the orchard i.e. greater than 1 Typh per 2 leaves, these thresholds can be raised*

Rosy apple aphid damage; a major pest in young orchards

The table below gives a general guide to the relative importance of a number of pests of cider apples. The list is not comprehensive but indicates which pests are most likely to cause economic damage if infestations are allowed to establish.

Key pests - those which need controlling if present	Potentially serious pests – regular assessment and spraying according to thresholds	Minor pests – Those which only occasionally require control measures
Apple sawfly Rosy-apple aphid	Apple blossom weevil Apple sucker Fruit tree red spider mite Rust mite Winter moth	Other aphids Apple ermine moth Apple leaf midge Capsids Clay-coloured weevil Codling moth Flat scarlet mite Leaf hoppers Scale insects Tortrix moths Woolly aphid

Damage caused by pests

Apple blossom weevil	can significantly reduce fruit set through damage to blossoms
Apple ermine moth	heavy infestations of caterpillars can result in significant defoliation and yield reduction; fruit bud strength for the following year will also be reduced. Difficult to control due to extensive webbing
Apple sawfly	may cause substantial fruit drop shortly after blossom, resulting in serious crop loss. Additionally, the fallen fruitlets begin brown rot build-up on the ground
Apple sucker	reduces fruit set, sometimes severely, by weakening blossom and preventing flowers from opening normally
Capsids	fruit damage is unimportant, but shoot damage on young trees can restrict shoot development
Clay-coloured weevil	Adult weevils graze the bark/rind of first and second year extension growth and may kill shoot tips. Normally only important in very young orchards
Codling moth	direct fruit damage is of little consequence, but it allows entry of brown rot and increases the build-up of rotten fruit on the ground

Flat scarlet mite	damage to leaves shows as yellowing and bronzing, particularly close to petiole and alongside the main veins. In heavy infestations, leaf drop and reduced yields occur, both in the current and following season
Leaf midge	feeds on expanding leaves of the young vegetative shoots and can delay the development the framework of young trees. Not important on mature trees
Fruit tree red spider mite	damage to leaves causes serious bronzing and even defoliation. Heavy infestations can cause significant tree stress and reduced yields, both in the current and following season
Rosy-apple aphid	builds-up very rapidly early in the season to cause severe crop loss through fruit size reduction. Population normally falls rapidly from late June and after this effect on yield is minimal. The aphid also restricts extension growth and the risk of damage on young trees may continue into late summer
Rust mite	damage to leaves causes serious bronzing and even defoliation. Causes significant tree stress, reducing yields in both the current and the following year
Scale insects	several different species; where numbers build up on branches and shoots they cause a rapid decline in vigour and cropping potential
Tortrix moths	caterpillars of various species cause blossom, leaf and fruit damage. Young trees particularly susceptible. Caterpillars of the fruitlet mining tortrix moth and the light brown apple moth may mine into fruit, increasing fruit rotting at harvest
Winter moth	caterpillars feed early in the season on blossom trusses and leaves causing direct crop loss
Woolly aphid	heavy infestations weaken trees and damage caused to bark allows entry of canker.

7.6.2 Approved pesticides

Refer to section 7.5 for general information.

- The approval status of a pesticide may change at any time. Ensure that pesticides used are approved at the time of application. If in doubt contact your supplier or adviser

- In order to discourage pests populations which are resistant to individual pesticides, avoid repeated use of the same product

- The product label will include the specific pests for which the product is approved so, unless there is a Specific Off-label Approval, only use against the specified pests
- With many pesticides, some incidental control of pests other than the target species can be expected.

7.6.3 Selective pesticides

Pesticides may at one extreme be broad-spectrum, i.e. control a wide range of pest types and species, and at the other, extremely selective, where they will only control one type of pest.

- When choosing a pesticide, always chose the most selective one which is active against the target pest
- The use of broad-spectrum pesticides will harm a wide range of both neutral and beneficial invertebrates
- However, where several pest species are a problem, using a broad-spectrum pesticide may reduce the number of individual treatments needed
- The more broad-spectrum a pesticide is, the more harm it will do to beneficial invertebrates
- Because of this harmful effect on beneficials, using broad-spectrum pesticides may increase the level of certain pests (e.g. mites)
- Synthetic pyrethroids are usually extremely broad-spectrum and should only be used in exceptional circumstances.

7.6.4 Encouraging beneficial insects and mites in the orchard

Beneficial invertebrates, if allowed to thrive, will reduce many potential pest species to insignificant levels, thereby reducing the number of pesticide applications needed. Using selective pesticides (see above) and providing a diverse habitat in and around the orchard are the best ways of encouraging beneficials.

- Avoid using broad-spectrum pesticides in the orchard
- When the crop is in flower only use pesticides which are safe to bees
- Before applying insecticides, mow alleys to reduce flowers on herbaceous plants as these attract both pollinating insects and beneficials such as hoverflies and anthocorids
- Always ensure that pesticide applications are accurately applied to the target and not allowed to drift onto other areas
- Follow the guidelines in sections 12.3 and 12.4 to enhance the habitat diversity around the orchard
- Avoid the use of translocated herbicides in the alleyways; this will allow establishment of flowering herbaceous plants

Preserve beneficial pollinating insects. Be careful not to spray insecticides when other plants are in flower

- Avoid spillage of fertiliser onto alleyways, excess fertility encourages invasive and competitive weed species which will also reduce bio-diversity

- Minimise the width of herbicide strips as far as possible, but on young trees remember that grass is competitive for both water and nutrients.

7.7 Disease control

Unlike with dessert and culinary apples, diseases which purely affect fruit quality and storage are usually of little importance in cider apple production. Diseases affecting the foliage and the roots and trunk however are of major importance and need to be controlled or avoided as far as possible. Disease control is normally associated with the use of fungicides, but variety choice (see Section 4.1), quality of planting material (see Section 4.5), site selection (see Section 3) and site preparation (see Section 5.1) can all have a major impact on the level of disease in the orchard.

- Regular orchard monitoring for disease presence and level must be carried out through the growing season

- The decision to apply a fungicide should be based on disease risk taking into account varietal susceptibility, weather risk, disease inoculum level and orchard assessments

- Fungicides which will have the minimum effect on beneficial insects and mites, should be selected

- Ensure tree guards and ties do not cut into the bark
- Cut ties and remove stakes altogether once trees are adequately anchored
- Paint major cuts with an approved paint immediately after pruning
- Stake and tie young trees securely to prevent rocking. This helps to protect the roots and crown of the tree from damage
- Ensure good drainage is maintained throughout the life of the orchard by keeping drains in good order and appropriate use of sub-soiling
- To minimise the risk of disease to the blossoms, fruit and leaves, maintain good air circulation through the canopy by regular attention to pruning both the trees and any surrounding windbreaks.
- Optimise fertilizer applications to avoid excessive shoot growth
- Top-up micronutrients with foliar applications when required
- Avoid tree stress such as over-cropping or the build-up of high levels of disease
- Remove or crush by rolling, any rotten fruit left after harvest
- Always follow the pesticide label instructions

7.7.1 Diseases, management and cultural control

No detailed studies have been done for cider apples as they have for culinary and dessert apples, to establish thresholds above which fungicide treatment would give an economic benefit to cider apple production. The guidelines given below are based on field experience over many seasons for the two major foliage diseases, apple mildew and apple scab, found in cider apple orchards.

Disease levels must be assessed by regular whole-orchard monitoring. The recorded results in combination with the predicted disease pressure (based on current and predicted weather), should form the basis of spray decisions.

Apple scab

Apple scab is the most economically important disease of cider apples; leaf scab depresses productivity, severely affected fruits are smaller and the scab lesions provide entry points for rots such as brown rot. Cider apple varieties vary in susceptibility; Michelin and Tremlett's Bitter are very susceptible; Brown's Apple can be susceptible and Somerset Redstreak and Ashton Bitter the most resistant.

The apple scab fungus over-winters mainly on leaves on the orchard floor, but can also survive on buds, shoot bases and wood as wood scab. The source of inoculum varies with variety, region and season. In spring spores infect developing leaves and fruit during wet weather to initiate the new scab epidemic to infect other new leaves and fruit. Successful control of apple scab combines cultural control, orchard monitoring and disease warning systems in an integrated approach to minimise fungicide inputs.

- Develops most rapidly in warm wet weather, with prolonged leaf wetness (even heavy dew) giving the highest risk
- Although mainly a disease of leaf and fruit, apple scab can infect the woody tissue (wood scab) and this will provide a constant source of new infection
- Wood scab develops mainly on trees where leaf scab infections are allowed to reach very high levels
- Where possible, where over-wintered leaf litter is excessive, to encourage their breakdown, macerate leaves by mowing after leaf fall during early winter
- Apply the first spray promptly at bud burst using a protectant fungicide also active against *Nectria* canker
- Scab control between bud burst and petal fall is most important
- Make use of scab warnings, such as ADEM, to optimise fungicide use
- Where fungicides are applied in response to a scab warning, choose a fungicide which has a curative or kick-back action
- Ensure scab fungicides from different chemical groups are used to avoid the development of fungicide resistance
- Scab sprays are not normally needed after the end of June unless early control was poor
- Where possible, after harvest and before leaf fall, spray 5% urea to encourage leaf rotting. This makes leaves more palatable to earthworms and also disrupts the overwintering stage of the scab fungus
- During winter pruning, check for and cut out any wood scab found on young trees

Apple mildew

Powdery mildew, although less of a problem in cider orchards than with other types of apples, can be an important disease, especially in the drier Midland counties. It can reduce yield and quality, particularly on susceptible varieties such as Somerset Redstreak, Dabinett and Ashton Bitter. Heavy infection will kill terminal buds, giving rise to excessive lateral production.

The fungus over-winters in buds which emerge in spring as mildewed blossoms or shoot tips. Spores from these infect developing flowers, leaves and shoots to initiate the secondary mildew epidemic. Control strategies depend on thorough monitoring and maintaining primary mildew at a low level, since once primary mildew levels are high, effective control becomes difficult.

- Fungicide inputs for control of mildew will depend on the susceptibility of the variety. On susceptible varieties and on young orchards, regular fungicide sprays will be required from pink bud to the end of shoot growth
- Adopt a flexible approach in which fungicide dose, spray interval and spray volume are adjusted to match the levels of epidemic activity

- Where primary mildew levels are high in young orchards, prompt physical removal of mildewed blossoms or shoots may be possible
- Practise good disease resistance management (see Section 7.7.3)

Blossom wilt

Blossom wilt can be a serious disease in cider apple orchards, especially on very susceptible varieties such as Somerset Redstreak or Stembridge Clusters, when it can cause significant losses.

The fungus overwinters on cankers and dead blossoms which produce spores in spring ready to infect flowers. The fungus attacks flowers causing them to wilt and can cause spur cankers. Blossom wilt can be confused with fireblight and other disease and pest problems (Table below). Routine treatments are not required every season

- Monitor orchards of susceptible varieties during late blossom and petal fall for dead/wilting trusses
- Where a problem occurs plan to treat the following season with an approved fungicide at first flower and then again 7-10 days later
- Post infection treatments are ineffective

Diagnosis of wilting dying blossoms

Disease/Problem	Blossom symptom	Fruiting bodies	Smell	Other symptoms
Blossom wilt (*Monilinia laxa f.sp. mali*)	Wilting/brown, Internal browning/necrosis	Grey pustules on infected parts	Foetid smell, similar to scent of sweet chestnut flowers	Disease progression into spur and branch forming cankers
Apple canker (*Nectria galligena*)	Wilting/brown, no internal browning	None	None	Nectria canker somewhere on branch with wilting blossoms
Fireblight (*Erwinia amylovora*)	Wilting/brown, internal browning/necrosis	Milky bacterial ooze on infected flower parts	None	Disease progression into spur and branch, possible further ooze
Bud moth (*Spilonota ocellana*)	Wilting/brown blossom. Hollow	None	None	Evidence of internal mining, caterpillar and frass

Apple Canker

Apple canker is an important disease of cider apples, particularly during establishment of new orchards. Canker tends to be much more serious in the wetter parts of the country and on higher land. Spores are produced all year round and can infect through wounds at any time. Wet seasons, particularly wet autumns favour its spread. Effective control of canker requires an integrated approach.

- In winter, prune out cankers where possible or pare back cankers on scaffold branches to healthy tissue

- Macerated prunings may be a source of inoculum for tree infection. If possible prunings should be removed and burnt

- In summer on young trees, prune out shoot dieback as soon as possible to reduce inoculum

- Ensure wounds are treated with an approved canker paint

- In problem orchards or in high-risk situations, apply sprays of a recommended fungicide at 10% leaf fall and 50% leaf fall to protect leaf scars against canker infection

- Chose a bud burst scab spray which is also active against canker, and repeat at mouse ear.

- Where canker is a real problem continue to use a dual-purpose fungicide for scab and canker through and after blossom

Crown rot

Crown rot is mainly a disease of trees in the early years of establishment (2 – 6 years), but its incidence is difficult to predict. The roots and crown of the tree are attacked but foliar symptoms may be the first indication of an infection. In its mild form, symptoms may be poor growth and leaf yellowing, but this may progress. The trees will die later if the rootstock is badly infected. Crown rot is caused by a soil-borne fungus – *Phytophthora cactorum* - that can survive in the soil as resting spores (oospores) in the absence of apple trees. Crown rot is favoured by wet soil conditions and consequently is easily confused with root and tree death which occurs when roots are waterlogged for significant periods.

- The are no effective chemical controls for crown rot

- Minimise the risk of crown rot by careful site selection, good soil drainage, rootstock selection and adequate staking and tying of young trees

- Trees showing severe foliar symptoms caused by crown rot will usually die. Severely affected trees should be grubbed and burnt, and the replanted tree treated with a recommended fungicide

Fireblight

On mature cider trees, especially those that flower late such as Brown Snout and Vilberie, fireblight infection results in some blossom death and shoot dieback but does not usually result in tree death. However young cider apple trees are more susceptible and infection may result in their death. Fireblight symptoms can be confused with those of other diseases (see Table above)

- There are no recommended chemical control measures
- The risk of fireblight is greatest when temperatures exceed 18°C and there is rain
- Monitor hedgerow hawthorn and susceptible ornamentals in adjacent gardens for signs of the disease
- For young trees in areas where fireblight problems have occurred previously, make regular routine inspections for fireblight symptoms from about mid-June to early August
- On young trees remove and burn affected parts as soon as possible, cutting back to healthy tissue well below the diseased (stained) wood

Reducing rotting in cider apples

Fungal rots reduce fruit yield and quality and hence the value of the juice. Efficient cider production requires fruit in good condition to be received at the factory. Cider makers may reject consignments or apply a penalty where excessive rotting is present. Most fungal rots in cider apples are caused by either brown rot or *Phytophthora sp.* The brown rot fungus invades fruit through wounds and rot can then spread to adjacent fruit by contact. Studies in cider orchards have shown that most entry wounds on fruit are caused by insect damage, especially codling moth and sawfly. *Phytophthora* is a soil-borne fungus and infects fruit when it comes into contact with wet soil. Losses due to brown rot, *Phytophthora* and other rots can be minimised by:

- Removing over-wintering inoculum in rotten or mummified fruits on the ground or in the tree
- Minimising soil contamination of fruit by permitting grass cover under the trees or by reducing the width of the herbicide strip
- Minimising damage to fruit by controlling sawfly and possibly codling moth
- Prompt harvest and rapid despatch of the fruit to the factory, especially when the weather is warm and wet

7.7.2 Approved fungicides

Refer to section 7.5 for general information.

- The approval status of a fungicide may change at any time.
- Ensure that fungicides used are approved at the time of application. If in doubt contact your supplier or adviser

- In order to minimise the risk of selection of disease populations which are resistant to individual fungicides, avoid repeated use of the same product or of products from the same chemical group (see next section)

- The product label will include the specific diseases for which the product is approved, and, unless there is a Specific Off-label Approval, only use against the specified diseases

- Some fungicides may have a suppressant effect on diseases other than those specified on the label. Such activity should be taken into account as it may mean fewer different fungicide treatments may be needed, particularly if disease pressure is low.

7.7.3 Resistance management

There has been a gradual increase in the occurrence of resistance since the introduction of the first systemic fungicides in the 1970s. These chemicals, unlike older materials, have very specific modes of action and strains of disease, resistant to the mode of action, are more easily selected. Regular use of one fungicide, or of fungicides of the same chemical group, has been proven to significantly speed-up the occurrence of resistant strains of fungi.

- Minimise the routine use of fungicides by using thresholds and disease prediction to trigger treatments

- Rotate applications of fungicides from different groups

- Avoid or, if there are no alternatives, minimise use of fungicides with only one mode of action

- Products containing more than one active ingredient against one disease, or some specifically recommended fungicide tank mixes, will help minimise the impact and occurrence of resistance

- As far as possible, reduce disease carry-over from year-to-year by encouraging natural break-down of dead leaves and fruit

The main groups of fungicides relevant to cider apples are the 'triazole' group, the strobilurines (QoI) and the anilinopyrimidines

The triazole group includes: -	Systhane (myclobutanil)
	Topas (penconazole)
The strobilurines include:-	Stroby (kresoxim-methyl)
	Bellis (pyraclostrobin + boscalid)
The anilinopyrimidines include:-	Scala (pyrimethanil)
	Switch (cyprodonil + fludioxonil)

7.8 Weed control

Any other plant growing within the rooting zone of a tree will compete with the tree for nutrients and water. On mature trees, particularly in standard orchards, this competition will have little or no effect on fruit yield. On young trees, weed competition is significant and will slow tree growth, delay maturity and reduce yields. Maintaining a weed-free strip along the tree rows will minimise this competition and is also very important for mechanical harvesting where blowers are used.

See Sections 6.2 and 6.6 for information on grass/alley maintenance with grazing and mowing.

- Perennial weeds should be controlled before planting a new orchard
- In the first 2 years after planting, do not allow any weed growth under the tree
- In bush orchards maintain a weed-free strip under the trees to minimise competition and to aid harvesting
- When the trees are mature, the herbicide strip should be as narrow as possible but compatible with the harvesting method
- If using herbicides for maintenance of the weed-free strip, choose contact or translocated herbicides
- Before establishing grass/tumble-down alleys, control invasive perennial weeds
- Where chemical weed control is to be used, consider spot treatment rather than overall application
- In established alleys, apart from mowing, the only weed control needed will be for control of invasive or competitive weeds
- When applying herbicides avoid spray drift onto any part of the tree; contact and translocated herbicides will damage tree foliage
- On young trees the trunk/branch bark is very susceptible to contact and translocated herbicides and the whole tree may be damaged
- Avoid use of any herbicides in field margins and hedgerows
- Application of an approved herbicide in mid-summer to control the grass, especially creeping bent (*Agrostis stolonifera*), on the borders of the alleyways, will help facilitate harvesting.

7.8.1 Approved herbicides

Refer to section 7.5 for general information.

- The approval status of a herbicide may change at any time. Ensure that herbicides used are approved at the time of application. If in doubt contact your supplier or adviser
- The product label may include specific weeds for which the product is approved, and, unless there is a Specific Off-label Approval, only use against the specified weeds
- Contact herbicides effectively only burn-off the foliage and only kill plants with small fibrous root systems

- Plants with tap or rhizome-type roots will usually re-grow following contact herbicide usage
- Translocated herbicides are absorbed into the plant and travel through it via the sap and/or water transport systems
- Translocated herbicides will usually kill plant roots, preventing regeneration
- Residual herbicides are persistent in the soil
- Most residual herbicides act by preventing seed germination and are therefore mainly used against annual weeds
- Most residual herbicides do not affect established weeds
- Because residual herbicides are subject to leaching and may contaminate ground water (streams and ditches etc.), it is good agricultural practice to only use them where there is no effective alternative.

7.8.2 Other methods of weed control

Apart from chemical weed control, various physical methods of weed control are available and their characteristics are listed below: -

Cultivation
- Is a good option on very young trees
- Must be shallow to minimise damage to the tree's fibrous roots
- Will not easily control perennial weeds
- Needs to be repeated regularly according to weed growth

Mulches
- Conserve moisture and can aid tree establishment
- Organic mulches may reduce nitrogen availability
- Loose organic mulches (e.g. straw or FYM) cannot be used where mechanical harvesting is used
- Artificial mulches such as Mypex or paper, can be used, but tend to be expensive and are difficult to replace in established orchards
- Mulches can provide good shelter for small rodents, which may then damage trunk bases and shallow roots

Heat (flame guns etc.)
- Can give very good control of small weeds
- Gives poor control of perennial weeds
- Needs to be repeated regularly according to weed growth
- On young trees may damage the fibrous root system close to the soil surface
- Take care to avoid damage to the tree trunk, particularly on young trees
- Tends to be very expensive and is very slow.

CHAPTER 8

Harvest, collection and transport

Having taken care to grow the crop to the highest standards, it is vital that the harvesting process is as efficient as possible and that the fruit is delivered to the factory in good condition with minimal contamination. The harvesting process is the area of cider apple production where the greatest economic losses can occur.

- Ensure that all equipment needed for the harvest process is available and in good working order well before harvest is due to start

- Arrange the required additional labour well in advance

- Prepare the grass sward by mowing/ceasing grazing at the appropriate time

- Schedule the picking rota for each orchard

- Reduce fruit damage by keeping handling to a minimum and by harvesting before fruit becomes over-ripe

- Take particular care to minimise contamination with soil and foreign bodies

- After harvest clean and service all equipment and make good any damage to the alleys, headlands and roadways caused in the harvesting process.

Left; Bruised and rotten, mud-contaminated fruit is not acceptable. Right; slight knocks are tolerable on clean, sound fruit

8.1 Maintaining Juice quality

Seasonal environmental factors are likely to cause more variation in juice quality than varietal and management factors. This especially applies to sugar content and to a lesser extent acidity and phenolics. As with any fruit, apple juice sugar correlates positively with hours of sunshine throughout the growing season and may vary by as much as 50% between variety and season. Persistent wet weather during August and September has a strong diluting influence on juice concentration. However there are several cultural and management practices that will influence juice quality.

- High rates of nitrogen applied either by foliar spray or to the ground will increase both fruit juice nitrogen levels and the subsequent rate of fermentation.

- Fruit juice phenolic content is inversely proportional to nitrogen levels; the higher the nitrogen, the lower the phenolic content. This is often why fruit from old trees in traditional orchards with low fertilizer input have better juice quality than well fed bush trees.

- For optimum juice quality it is recommended to apply minimal nitrogen feeding required for reasonable growth.

8.1.1 Testing for Residual Starch

At optimum maturity the apples will have the maximum sugar content, full potential flavour and aroma, and will lack the potential for producing the 'off-flavours' typical of over-ripe fruit. As fruit approaches maturity the stored solid starch content is rapidly converted to soluble sugars. The presence of residual starch is easily detected by dipping a halved fruit in dilute iodine solution. Any starch will quickly turn the surface blue. Fully ripened fruit will show no discolouration.

Fruit picked too early will have a poor sugar content. Best results are obtained from fruit harvested just before full maturity. At this stage it will maintain its firmness and resilience to mechanical harvesting, be in optimum conditions for maximum juice extraction on pressing, but will retain little starch.

Fruit harvested at stage 3 – 2 will still be firm enough to resist bruising'

8.2 Harvest scheduling

- Plan to harvest each orchard according to the variety and earliness of the individual site
- Liaise with your customer(s), i.e. the cider maker, about optimum picking dates
- Maintain regular contact with your customer throughout the harvesting period to ensure your deliveries can be accepted
- Be prepared to amend harvest plans according to circumstances
- Fruit deteriorates very slowly when still on the tree
- Fruit shaken or fallen deteriorates quicker due to damage/bruising
- Collect fruit as soon as possible after shaking to reduce deterioration
- Fruit harvested and stored in heaps will deteriorate extremely rapidly
- Aim for the fruit to be stored in heaps for no more than 24 hours before delivery to the factory
- Mechanically harvested fruit may be picked slightly under-ripe
- Do not allow the fruit to become over-ripe
- Where orchards contain more than one variety, each variety may need to be picked separately at its optimum time.
- So that fruit may ripen earlier and more uniformly, consider using an approved chemical ripening agent for early cultivars (e.g. Browns Apple, Michelin)
- This treatment is very temperature dependant and is best completed before the night temperatures begin to fall in late September.

8.3 Ground preparation

Good ground preparation prior to harvest is vital to minimise contamination of harvested fruit and to allow efficient mechanical collection of fruit.

- Level/avoid wheel ruts in alleyways where mechanical fruit collection will be done
- Where orchards are grazed, stock must be removed at least 56 days before the start of harvest
- Where footpaths pass through orchards, erect notices advising of the harvest operation and requesting dog owners not to allow dogs free-run in the orchard and to remove their dogs' faeces
- Mowing alleys too close to harvest will exacerbate grass contamination of the fruit
- Mechanical harvesters are very inefficient in long grass
- Mow alleys about 4 weeks before harvest, dependant on growing conditions, to provide optimum environment for a clean and efficient harvest
- Where fruit is due to be mechanically collected, before tree shaking, check the orchard and remove prunings, stones and all other potential contaminants

8.4 Hand harvesting

Harvesting by hand will generally result in the best quality fruit, but is extremely expensive and is only practical today on young trees and on small areas.

* Minimise the distance pickers have to carry picked apples by providing bulking facilities at regular intervals
* See also Section 8.6.

8.5 Tree shaking

To aid or stimulate the fall of ripe fruit, hand or mechanical tree shaking can be used. Tree shaking is only effective when the fruit starts to ripen and becomes easier to dislodge. Mechanical tree shakers provide a very efficient way of harvesting apples from larger and mature trees.

* Shaking should be done as close as possible to the expected time of collection/pick-up of the fruit from the ground
* For varieties ripening over a long period it may be necessary to shake (and collect) more than once over several weeks

Shaking by hand

* This is only practical on young or small trees
* Poles must be used with care to minimise damage to small branches and spurs that would reduce subsequent crops
* There is a significantly increased risk of diseases such as canker developing on cuts and abrasions caused by the use of poles
* Using hooked poles (similar to a shepherd's crook) to pull and shake will cause less damage than using poles to hit branches to dislodge the fruit.

Mechanical shaking

* Before using a mechanical shaker check that the cushioning pads on the clamps are in place, appropriately lubricated and sound
* Check cushioning pads regularly during each working session
* If used carelessly mechanical shakers can cause serious damage to the trunk bark and allow entry of diseases such as canker, silver leaf and *Phytophthora*
* Young trees are particularly susceptible to root and trunk damage
* Tree guards and stakes may interfere with effective operation of mechanical shakers
* Fixed-arm shakers are slower than swing-arm types
* Fixed-arm shakers are positioned by manoeuvring the tractor and therefore result in more sward damage and soil compaction than swing-arm types where the tractor is able to travel straight along the alleyway
* Always ensure that the clamp is securely gripped onto the trunk before starting to shake

- Ensure that the clamp is set at the optimum height, high enough to transmit the vibration up into the canopy, but not too high to cause excessive vibration to the root system.
- Belt shakers are less expensive to buy but are hard work, requiring two operators and can cause damage to tree bark.

8.6 Fruit collection

Fruit which has fallen or been shaken onto the ground is inevitably bruised and will start to deteriorate quickly. Certain fungi which cause fruit rotting (e.g. *Phytophthora*), are present in the soil and these infect damaged tissue, so the longer fruit is left uncollected the greater the losses will be.

- Where no tree shaking is used it may be necessary to collect several times to avoid too many rotten fruit from contaminating others
- Collect as soon as possible after shaking
- Even with tree-shaking, more than one collection may be needed with certain cider apple cultivars which ripen over a long period
- Fruit collection from the orchard floor can be done by hand or using one of three different basic types of machine
- Mechanical harvesters will not collect apples efficiently from wheel ruts

Hand collection

- Labour for collection by hand is expensive and is in very short supply
- Hand collection is only practical on young trees or on very small areas
- Bags used for collection and the bins used for bulking must not have been used for storage or carriage of any toxic or hazardous material or any livestock or livestock products.

Pedestrian –steered self-propelled machines

- These are comparatively labour-intensive but are suitable and efficient for small areas
- This type of machine is suitable for standard orchards
- With heavy crops, moderate forward speed to reduce fruit damage
- The efficiency of hand-steered machine collection can be restricted by inadequate bulking facilities within the orchard
- Always provide plenty of boxes for use on the machine and also bins or mobile trailers for bulking fruit from the boxes
- Boxes used for collection on the machine and the bins/trailers used for bulking should have been cleaned before use and must not have been used for storage or carriage of any toxic or hazardous material or any livestock or livestock products
- These machines can normally collect apples from under tree canopy right up to trunk, reducing the need to blow apples towards the alleyway

- Before use check all guards and safety devices are in place and sound
- Always turn machine off before undertaking any maintenance or repairs
- Regularly check belts, paddles, pulleys and conveyors and if necessary clear them of leaves, twigs, mud and other potential blockages and contaminants.

Self-propelled integral machines

- Relatively expensive machines, but with a low labour requirement
- Ideal for small to medium sized areas but also suitable for the largest orchards, particularly before they reach full cropping
- With heavy crops the size of integral hopper may affect the machine's efficiency. Be sure to provide frequent bulking sites to avoid this potential problem
- To minimise fruit damage, particularly where crops are heavy, reduce the forward speed of machine and slow the speed of conveyors if possible
- This type of machine can usually collect apples from well under the tree canopy close to the trunk, allowing lower blower capacity to be used. Ensure pruning takes account of this facility by reducing low-hanging branches
- Before use check all guards and safety devices are in place and sound
- Always turn machine off before undertaking any maintenance or repairs
- Regularly check belts, paddles, pulleys and conveyors and if necessary clear them of leaves, twigs, mud and other potential blockages and contaminants.

Tractor powered/mounted machines

- For maximum efficiency apples should be collected in a detachable trailer
- Ensure adequate supply of empty trailers on headlands
- These machines need more turning space on headlands than other types of machine
- Before starting collection it may be necessary to blow, brush or mechanically sweep apples from under the trees into the alleyway
- To minimise fruit damage moderate the forward speed of machine and slow the speed of conveyors if possible
- Keep the height from which apples are dropped into trailers from conveyors to the minimum possible
- Before use check all guards and safety devices are in place and sound
- Always turn machine off before undertaking any maintenance or repairs
- Regularly check belts, paddles, pulleys and conveyors and if necessary clear them of leaves, twigs, mud and other potential blockages and contaminants.

Collect fruit as soon as possible after shaking.

8.7 Washing and storing

Washing fruit will reduce the amount of contamination transported to the factory, but washed fruit tends to deteriorate quicker than unwashed fruit. Some cider makers request that fruit is not washed before delivery.

- Check with your customer regarding their policy on washing fruit after harvest
- Ideally use clean water for washing
- If re-circulated water is used, allow major sediment to settle out before re-use
- Fruit brought from the orchard should be stored on a clean solid pad, ideally of concrete or asphalt
- Pads must never be used for storage of any toxic or hazardous materials including animals, animal waste, animal carcases, animal feed, fertilisers, pesticides, agricultural seed treated with pesticides, domestic or industrial waste or any item which may have been contaminated with a chemical classified as harmful, dangerous or toxic

- The storage pad should be cleaned immediately before harvest commences using a pressure washer and a food-grade disinfectant or detergent
- To reduce bruising minimise the drop height from trailers and conveyors onto the storage pad
- Fruit should be kept in heaps on the pad for as short a time as possible, ideally less than 24 hours, before transport to the factory
- Debris such as sticks, leaves, grass and stones are not acceptable and must be removed from the fruit before despatch to the factory

8.8 Transport to factory

Most cider makers have a quota system for accepting deliveries and it is essential to make the necessary arrangements well before the start of harvest. Some cider makers will have a Code of Practice for fruit delivery. Growers need to be aware of any such codes and to adhere to them. The harvested fruit is a food product and as such is covered by additional legislation. The Food Safety (General Food Hygiene) Regulations 1995 is the legislation most relevant to the transport of cider apples.

- Ensure delivery drivers adhere to the cider makers site regulations, particularly those relating to safety issues
- Where possible use transport facilities constructed with a sound, smooth, inert and easily cleaned material
- Trailers/containers constructed or lined with metal are more easily cleaned than wood lined ones but they may cause more fruit bruising
- Apart from toxic and hazardous chemicals, other high risk materials which transport containers must be free from include residues from livestock and poultry (live or dead), processed animal protein, domestic and industrial waste, animal and poultry waste including manures and composts
- Consult your customer for full details of requirements for transport facilities
- Trailers etc should be thoroughly and appropriately cleaned before use for transporting cider apples
- Trailers etc should be washed out between loads of cider apples to avoid build-up of contaminants
- Where sacks/bags are used to carry fruit they must be clean and never have been used for toxic or hazardous materials
- Once used for cider fruit, bags/sacks should be retained for this use exclusively.

CHAPTER 9

Pollution control and waste management

9.1 Pesticide use and storage

Pesticide labels include detailed guidance and instructions on avoiding polluting non-target areas. Inefficient sprayers or careless sprayer use can cause significant pollution, but inappropriate disposal of pesticides and their containers produce some of the major pollution incidents. It is the responsibility of employers to manage staff closely and for both employers and employees to ensure all regulations are adhered to at all times.

- Avoid routine pesticide applications, assess the risk of economic damage before treatment

- Always read the pesticide label before use and note environmental restrictions and advice

- Undertake a LERAP to establish the need for a buffer zone

- Direct the spray nozzles at the target to avoid drift

- When spraying along headlands avoid spraying towards, or allowing spray to drift onto, the field margins

- Spray drift is always highest when wind speed exceeds 6.5km/h (4mph, Force2) and spraying should stop above this wind speed

- The nozzles used in air-assisted sprayers produce a fine spray which can cause drift of considerable distances in calm conditions; so avoid spraying in very calm conditions

- A well-maintained and correctly used sprayer will achieve better spray coverage, reduce drift and achieve more cost-effective crop protection

- Pesticides must be stored under cover in a locked frost-free building, or custom- made container, either bunded or with an impervious floor

- Where spraying operations are remote from the main storage site, pesticides should be transported in their original containers in a secure container able to contain any spillage

- Never leave pesticides unattended in the field

- Return all pesticides and containers at the end of each spraying session to the main store

- Pesticide packaging deteriorates over time. Old unwanted pesticides should be disposed of correctly and not stored indefinitely (see 9.2 below).

9.2 Disposal of pesticide and other toxic waste

Toxic waste disposal is covered by a number of Acts relating to the environment and to groundwater. New guidelines and codes of practice are regularly produced, particularly by the Environment Agency, so make sure you are up-to-date.

Avoidance of production of toxic waste should be a priority for growers

* Only mix sufficient pesticides for the area to be sprayed
* Only buy sufficient pesticides for immediate needs.

Unused diluted pesticides, or tank washings: -

* can be applied to crops provided that such an application does not contravene the terms of the Approval of the pesticide(s)
* may be stored in a container or water-tight sump pending disposal by an licensed waste disposal contractor
* with an authorisation from the Environment Agency certain diluted pesticides may be sprayed onto a designated area of non-cropping land.

Unwanted undiluted pesticides: -

* must never be removed or decanted from their original containers but stored for later disposal
* in some circumstances may be returned to the supplier (this should be the preferred choice)
* even if the pesticide is still approved for the crop, it may be inadvisable to use it up on the crop (e.g. if resistance is a problem or there are alternative, safer, more selective products)
* there are a number of licensed specialist waste disposal companies and these will need to be employed for disposal of pesticides and other toxic wastes.

Empty pesticide containers are regarded as toxic waste and must be disposed of correctly.

* Burning or burial of empty pesticide containers is not permitted
* Some containers may be returnable and this is the favoured method of disposal
* Liquid containers should be triple-rinsed into the spray tank
* After cleaning they should be stored separately and securely away from other waste
* Non-returnable containers should be punctured to avoid re-use
* Containers of dry formulations should be stored securely with the empty and rinsed liquid containers
* Some licensed land fill sites will take clean empty pesticide containers, check if there is a local one, otherwise use a licensed waste disposal contractor.

9.3 Disposal of non-toxic waste

- Minimise your waste by buying materials in returnable or re-cycleable containers
- Waste plant material can easily be re-cycled if chipped and composted or used as a mulch
- Most paper and cardboard can and should be re-cycled
- Increasingly plastics can be recycled and some waste disposal companies offer special services.

9.4 Apple washings, washings debris and storage heap liquor

After harvest before delivery to the factory, recycled water from washing apples will become contaminated with suspended and dissolved substances. Such water can be very harmful to an aquatic environment and should never be allowed to contaminate watercourses, springs, ponds or ditches. Use of a slurry spreader on non-cropping land or un-grazed grassland provides the safest way of disposal. Ensure any spreading does not come within 10 metres of a watercourse, or 50 metres of a spring or borehole.

Solid debris from the washing process (leaves, soil, rotten apples etc) can be very toxic if stored in heaps. Either spread thinly on un-cropped land or dispose of as toxic waste.

The liquid (liquor) running out of apple storage heaps can become extremely concentrated and must never be allowed to run into ditches or water courses. To avoid contamination, pads for apple heaps should not be sited close to cropped areas.

CHAPTER 10

Energy Efficiency

Although cider apple production, as opposed to cider making, is not a high energy-consuming operation, energy efficiency is a component of Integrated Crop Management and needs to be considered. Energy efficiency involves attempting to minimise the unnecessary use or wastage of natural resources.

- When planning new buildings maximise the use of insulation and make full use of natural light

- Machinery varies greatly in its energy efficiency. Plan new purchases with this in mind

- Inefficient machines may result in additional operations being needed

- Maintain existing machinery for maximum efficiency, including tyre pressure and ballast

- Install water storage tanks at remote sites to minimise sprayer movements.

CHAPTER 11

Health and Safety

Everyone from the land-owner through the employer and employee, even to the farm visitor and people using public rights of way have some H&S (Health and Safety) duties and responsibilities. However the biggest responsibility falls on the land-owner, the tenant farmer and the employer. The land-owner and tenant farmer must provide a safe environment for anyone who has cause to be on the farm.

The employer has the responsibility of providing appropriate training, guidance, management, supervision, equipment and facilities for all his or her staff, and to monitor their working practices regularly so that corrective action can be taken if needed.

Employers' responsibilities include ensuring that employees and contractors working on the farm are aware of the farm's H&S policy and that they are expected to follow all H&S legislation applicable to their work on the farm.

The Health and Safety at Work Act (1974) includes the obligation for employees and the self employed to take "reasonable care of their own health and safety whilst at work", also to take reasonable care that their acts or omissions do not affect third parties. The Management of H&S at Work Regulations 2009 details a number of other specific requirements, including the obligation to carry out risk assessments.

11.1 Pesticides

This section summarises the main issues relating to pesticides (more detail is included in Chapters 7&9). The main regulations covering the H&S aspects of use of pesticides are included in "The Food and Environment Protection Act 1985 (FEPA)" the "Control of Pesticides Regulations 1986 (COPR)" the "Plant Protection Products Regulations" (PPPR) and COSHH (see next section).

All agricultural pesticides used in the UK must be approved, the following website can be used to confirm if the pesticide is approved: http://www.pesticides.gov.uk/approvals.asp

Generally all staff involved in handling, storing, mixing or applying pesticides must have received appropriate training in pesticides safely, which includes the law, the risks to people, wildlife and the environment, safe working procedures, emergency procedures and related action plans such as what to do in the event of personal contamination, a spillage or a fire, also health monitoring, record keeping and using equipment to apply pesticides.

- Everyone who uses pesticides professionally must be formally trained, hold the necessary certificates of competence and records must be kept of such training

- A secure and appropriate pesticide store is required
- Operators must have their own protective clothing
- Protective clothing must be suitable and approved for the purpose and undamaged
- Health surveillance should be arranged for workers who frequently apply pesticides

11.2   COSHH

The COSHH (Control of Substances Hazardous to Health) Regulations 2002 were made under the Health and Safety at Work Act 1974. They cover most substances potentially hazardous to health including for example chemicals (e.g. pesticides), biological agents, fumes, vapours, mists, and dusts. Under the regulations the first consideration should be to avoid its use, then consider substituting this for a less hazardous substance. PPE (personal protective equipment) should be the last control measure considered. Employers must undertake a COSHH assessment for each hazardous substance potentially present in the workplace. COSHH requires you to:

- Assess the risks, start this process by obtaining a copy of the manufacturers MSDS (safety data sheet), before placing an order!, relying on the container label is not sufficient
- Decide what precautions are required
- Prevent or adequately control exposure
- Ensure that control measures are used and maintained
- Prepare plans for foreseeable accidents, incidents and emergency situations
- Ensure individuals are provided with appropriate information, instruction, training and supervision
- The assessment must be recorded in writing and made available for inspection
- Assessments must be periodically reviewed and if circumstances change
- In appropriate cases, monitoring of exposure and undertaking health surveillance may be necessary,

Records must be retained for at least 5 years. Some records such as health surveillance, or monitoring records representative of personal exposure of identifiable employees must be kept for at least 40 years.

11.3 Machinery

Use of machinery on farms presents the greatest health and safety risk and employers are responsible for the provision and maintenance of all machinery.

- Any machinery used must be suitable for the intended task

- Machinery must be regularly maintained according to the manufacturer's instructions, and be in good working order
- Anyone required to use machinery must be given the appropriate training and deemed competent, check their certification
- Under no circumstances should machinery be maintained whilst it is still energised
- All required guards and safety devices must be fitted, secure and regularly checked

11.4 Transport

Transport used on public highways to carry staff, equipment or goods must be maintained in accordance with the current road traffic regulations. Vehicles used for transport must only be used for the purpose for which they were designed. On the farm the employer should ensure that transport vehicles are safe for the purpose for which they are being used.

11.5 Staff facilities

Appropriate facilities must be provided for staff to undertake their work safely and shall comply with the Workplace Health, Safety and Welfare Regulations 1992 , for example:

- First Aid boxes should be present at all permanent sites and in the vicinity of fieldwork
- Adequate toilet and washing facilities must be available
- Particular hazards should be clearly identified by warning signs

11.6 Public access

The grower has the responsibility of care to the public using public footpaths etc.

- Public rights of way must be maintained to allow safe access, and stiles and bridges must be sound
- Farm equipment should not be left unattended close to rights of way
- Signs should be erected to warn of particular risks, including spray operations

In summary, compliance with legislation is the minimum standard accepted, we strongly recommend visiting the websites below and reading the guidance available:

www.pesticides.gov.uk
http://www.pesticides.gov.uk/approvals.asp
http://www.hse.gov.uk/agriculture/index.htm
www.environment-agency.gov.uk
http://www.businesslink.gov.uk/bdotg/action/home

Mixed hedges, flowering plants and long grasses in the orchard margins are an invaluable source of benficial insects

CHAPTER 12

Conservation

12.1 Whole farm conservation policy

Conservation, the maintenance of a diverse environment and minimising any negative impact of agricultural practices on the farm and adjoining land, must be dealt with for the whole farm. Cider apple orchards should form an integral part of the conservation policy, particularly on farms growing a high proportion of arable crops. Conservation is not just passive but needs to include positive efforts to improve the environment on the farm. A robust conservation policy will increase bio-diversity and will enhance the number of beneficial and neutral vertebrate and invertebrate species

- Start with an 'environmental audit,' the initial part of which is free (contact DEFRA)

- Environmental audits should not deal just with the impact on the farm but to the wider environment; including a carbon audit helps to broaden the scope of the environmental audit

- Develop a whole farm policy with help from a relevant specialist organisation such as FWAG

- The policy should include a timescale for action

- Review and update the policy annually

- Grant aid may be available to help with many types of conservation work

- Environmental Stewardship schemes, run by Natural England, cover conservation management on farms

- Entry Level Stewardship (ELS) is open to all farmers across all farm types

- More information about ELS is available from regional offices of Natural England and from independent advisers.

12.2 The orchard

The orchard itself should be regarded as a conservation resource and with appropriate management can add to the whole farm conservation value.

- When planning a new orchard leave room around the outside for rough grass margins

- When planning an orchard ensure that features of conservation value, such as ponds and mature trees, are preserved and incorporate them into your design

- Hang insect refuges in the apple trees to enable naturally-occurring predators such as lacewings, anthocorids and earwigs to over-winter within the orchard

- Young orchards may lack suitable old wood which hole-nesting birds require. Many of these birds are excellent predators of pests such as caterpillars. Install suitable nest boxes around the perimeter of the orchard
- Bats are voracious predators of night-flying insects, including several moth pests. Install bat boxes on mature headland trees.

12.3 Use of agrochemicals

Agrochemicals, including fertilisers, will always have side-effects on non-target species and areas. Minimise their impact by adhering strictly to the regulations on pesticide usage and to the guidelines for fertiliser application.

- Avoid the use of agrochemicals on, or drift onto, non-cropping areas and field margins
- Follow any buffer zones requirements for pesticides and conduct a LERAP assessment
- Fertiliser applications should be made only to the rooting zone of the trees avoiding spillage onto headlands and alleyways
- Empty pesticide containers and fertiliser bags should always be returned to a designated storage area pending appropriate disposal

12.4 Hedges and field margins

Field margins provide some of the best sources of biodiversity on many farms and should be managed to maximise this effect. Grass margins and hedges are equally important for different types of wildlife.

- Hedges should include a wide range of plant species
- Hedges should have a full, dense structure from ground level; grasses and herbaceous plants forming a lower storey, through mid-height shrubs, to the full canopy with small trees
- Stock can be very destructive to hedges, particularly the bottom of the hedge, so fence to prevent damage, where necessary
- Rodents, particularly rabbits, can be very damaging to hedges as well as to cider trees. Install a rabbit-proof fence outside the boundary hedge
- At the appropriate time hedges should ideally be layered to increase density
- To maximise the environment for birds, hedge-cutting should be done after the winter food (berries etc) has been exhausted but before nesting starts
- Each year leave some hedges untrimmed
- Rough grass margins provide valuable over-wintering habitat for many crop pollinators and predators
- Leave a strip of un-mown grass between the hedge and the orchard to encourage more herbaceous plant diversity.

12.5 Non-cropping areas

Non-cropping areas of the farm can provide some of the richest and most diverse habitats for wildlife. Woodland and ponds are the obvious examples, but field corners and small coppices provide refuges and are particularly useful when linked by hedges and other 'green' corridors. Even land temporarily taken out of use can provide a valuable habitat for a wide range of wildlife. However, a bare fallow has a negative effect on conservation.

- Include non-cropping areas in the whole farm conservation policy
- Do not just neglect non-cropping areas
- Actively manage non-cropping areas, but avoid any unnecessary interference.

APPENDIX I

Sources of further information
See also Appendix 111 for Legislation guides and codes of practice

Pests of Fruit Crops. A Colour Handbook, David V Alford (2007)

Cider and Juice Apples: Growing and Processing, edited R R Williams (1988)

Crop Protection Association/British Agrochemicals Association, various leaflets on pesticides in relation to conservation, food safety, water quality, COSHH, protective clothing etc.

Farming and Wildlife Advisory Group, various leaflets on conservation, pesticides, environment, hedges and field boundaries etc.

Fertiliser Recommendations for Agricultural and Horticultural Crops (RB209), MAFF (2000)

The Best Practice Guide for UK Apple Production, DEFRA (2002)

The LEAF Handbook for Integrated Farm Management, LEAF (2000)

The UK Pesticide Guide, CABI Publishing (new issue each year)

NACM Technical Reports
List of reports and copies available on application

APPENDIX II

Useful contacts and links

ADAS	0845 7660 085	www.adas.co.uk
BASIS		www.basis-reg.co.uk
BASF		www.agricentre.basf.co.uk
Bayer CropScience		www.bayercropscience.com
BCP Certis		www.epcertis.com
British Beekeepers Association		www.britishbee.org.uk
Crop Protection Association	01733 355 370	info@cropprotection.org.uk
DEFRA	0845 933 55 77	www.defra.gov.uk
		helpline@defra.gsi.gov.uk
EMR East Malling Research	01732 843833	www.emr.ac.uk
Environment Agency	0870 8506 506	www.environment-agency.gov.uk
FWAG	02476 696 699	www.fwag.org.uk
HDC		
Horticultural Development council		www.hdc.org.uk
HSE Health & Safety Executive		www.pesticides.gov.uk
LANTRA Training		www.lantra.co.uk
National Association of Cider Makers		www.cideruk.com
NACM	07761 874 277	
City & Guilds NPTC		www.nptc.org.uk
National Proficiency Test Council		
Natural England	0845 600 3078	www.naturalengland.org.uk
NFU	0247 685 8500	www.nfuonline.com

APPENDIX III

Relevant legislation and codes of practice

Code of practice for the safe use of pesticides on farms and holdings, (1998)

Code of good agricultural practice for the protection of water, PB 0587 (1998)

Code of good agricultural practice for the protection of soil, PB 0617 (1998)

Code of good agricultural practice for the protection of air, PB 0618 (1998)

Control of pesticides regulations 1986 (COPR) (amended 1997)

The control of pollution act 1974

The control of substances harmful to health regulations 1994 (COSHH)

Environment protection act 1990

Food and environment protection act 1985 (FEPA)

The food safety act 1990

Groundwater regulations 1998

Health and safety at work act 1974

Management of health and safety at work regulations 1994

The pesticides act 1998

The water resources act 1991

The wildlife and countryside act 1981

Wild mammals (protection) act 1996

APPENDIX IV

Nutrients and deficiency symptoms

NITRATE
Leaf analysis guideline range N 2.00 – 2.50%
Needed for all plant growth, leaves, flowers, fruits, shoots and roots.
Deficiency symptoms
Uniformly pale leaves. Small leaf size. Fruits often smaller and maturing earlier.
Nitrogen deficiency is accentuated by prolonged wet weather and light soils.
Sources (N or NO_3)
Ammonium nitrate (35%), urea (46%), sulphate of ammonia (48%), potassium nitrate (50%) etc.
Soil apply in two or three annual applications, before rainfall. Do not apply to young trees before they have begun to crop well.
Correct deficiencies with foliar sprays of urea or potassium nitrate.

POTASSIUM
Leaf analysis guideline range K 1.00 – 1.50%
Needed for cell division especially in fruits and flowers.
Deficiency symptoms
Marginal scorch of older leaves, dull brown or greyish, cupped. Small leaf size and reduced shoot growth.
Potash deficiency is accentuated by a heavy crops and acidic soils.
Sources (K_2O)
Muriate of potash (60%), sulphate of potash (48%), etc
Soil apply according to leaf or soil analysis.
Correct deficiencies with foliar sprays proprietary formulations or soluble potassium salt.

PHOSPHATE
Leaf analysis guideline level P 0.25%
Needed for root regeneration, photosynthesis, starch and sugar formation, chlorophyll etc. Usually available in the soil in adequate quantities.
Less available in acidic (below pH 6) or alkaline soils (above pH 7.5)
Sources (P_2O_5)
Water soluble; superphosphate (18%), triple superphosphate (47%)
Insoluble basic slag (18%)
Soil apply according to leaf or soil analysis.
Foliar spray as potassium phosphite to promote root regeneration.

MAGNESIUM
Leaf analysis guideline Mg 0.30%
Needed for chlorophyll and photosynthesis.
Deficiency symptoms